The Scarlet Letter

紅 字

· D ·

商務印書館

Name of Book: The Scarlet Letter
Author: Nathaniel Hawthorne
Text adaptation and activities: Gina D.B. Clemen
Editors: Rebecca Raynes, Elvira Poggi Repetto
Design and art direction: Nadia Maestri
Computer graphics: Simona Corniola
Illustrations: Gianni De Conno
Picture research: Laura Lagomarsino
Edition: ©2004 Black Cat Publishing
                 an imprint of Cideb Editrice, Genoa, Canterbury

系 列 名：Black Cat 優質英語階梯閱讀 · Level 6
書　　名：紅　字
責任編輯：黃淑嫻
封面設計：張　毅
出　　版：商務印書館（香港）有限公司
　　　　　香港筲箕灣耀興道 3 號東滙廣場 8 樓
　　　　　http://www.commercialpress.com.hk
印　　刷：中華商務彩色印刷有限公司
　　　　　香港新界大埔汀麗路 36 號中華商務印刷大廈
版　　次：2004 年 2 月第 1 版第 1 次印刷
　　　　　© 2004 商務印書館（香港）有限公司
　　　　　ISBN 962 07 1698 1
　　　　　Printed in Hong Kong

出版說明

　　本館一向倡導優質閱讀，近年來連續推出了以“Q”為標識的 “Quality English Learning 優質英語學習”系列，其中《讀名著學英語》叢書，更是香港書展入選好書，讀者反響令人鼓舞。推動社會閱讀風氣，推動英語經典閱讀，藉閱讀拓廣世界視野，提高英語水平，已經成為一種潮流。

　　然良好閱讀習慣的養成非一日之功，大多數初、中級程度的讀者，常視直接閱讀厚重的原著為畏途。如何給年輕的讀者提供切實的指引和幫助，如何既提供優質的學習素材，又提供名師的教學方法，是當下社會關注的重要問題。針對這種情況，本館特別延請香港名校名師，根據多年豐富的教學經驗，精選海外適合初、中級英語程度讀者的優質經典讀物，有系統地出版了這套叢書，名為《Black Cat 優質英語階梯閱讀》。

　　《Black Cat 優質英語階梯閱讀》體現了香港名校名師堅持經典學習的教學理念，以及多年行之有效的學習方法。既有經過改寫和縮寫的經典名著，又有富創意的現代作品；既有精心設計的聽、說、讀、寫綜合練習，又有豐富的歷史文化知識；既有彩色插圖、繪圖和照片，又有英美專業演員朗讀作品的 CD。適合口味不同的讀者享受閱讀之樂，欣賞經典之美。

　　《Black Cat 優質英語階梯閱讀》由淺入深，逐階提升，好像參與一個尋寶遊戲，入門並不難，但要真正尋得寶藏，需要投入，更需要堅持。只有置身其中的人，才能體味純正英語的魅力，領略得到真寶的快樂。當英語閱讀成為自己生活的一部分，英語水平的提高自然水到渠成。

商務印書館（香港）有限公司

編輯部

使用説明 _____

① 應該怎樣選書？

按閱讀興趣選書

《Black Cat 優質英語階梯閱讀》精選世界經典作品，也包括富於創意的現代作品；既有膾炙人口的小説、戲劇，又有非小説類的文化知識讀物，品種豐富，內容多樣，適合口味不同的讀者挑選自己感興趣的書，享受閱讀的樂趣。

按英語程度選書

《Black Cat 優質英語階梯閱讀》現設 Level 1 至 Level 6，由淺入深，涵蓋初、中級英語程度。讀物分級採用了國際上通用的劃分標準，主要以詞彙（vocabulary）和結構（structures）劃分。

Level 1 至 Level 3 出現的詞彙較淺顯，相對深的核心詞彙均配上中文解釋，節省讀者查找詞典的時間，以專心理解正文內容。在註釋的幫助下，讀者若能流暢地閱讀正文內容，就不用擔心這一本書程度過深。

Level 1 至 Level 3 出現的動詞時態形式和句子結構比較簡單。動詞時態形式以現在時（present simple）、現在時進行式（present continuous）、過去時（past simple）為主，句子結構大部分是簡單句（simple sentences）。此外，還包括比較級和最高級（comparative and superlative forms）、可數和不可數名詞（countable and uncountable nouns）以及冠詞（articles）等語法知識點。

Level 4 至 Level 6 出現的動詞時態形式，以現在完成時（present perfect）、現在完成時進行式（present perfect continuous）、過去完成時（past perfect continuous）為主，句子結構大部分是複合句（compound sentences）、條件從句（1st and 2nd conditional sentences）等。此外，還包括情態動詞（modal verbs）、被動形式（passive forms）、動名詞（gerunds）、

短語動詞（phrasal verbs）等語法知識點。

　　根據上述的語法範圍，讀者可按自己實際的英語水平，如詞彙量、語法知識、理解能力、閱讀能力等自主選擇，不再受制於學校年級劃分或學歷高低的約束，完全根據個人需要選擇合適的讀物。

② 怎樣提高閱讀效果？

　　閱讀的方法主要有兩種：一是泛讀，二是精讀。兩者各有功能，適當地結合使用，相輔相成，有事半功倍之效。

　　泛讀，指閱讀大量適合自己程度（可稍淺，但不能過深）、不同內容、風格、體裁的讀物，但求明白內容大意，不用花費太多時間鑽研細節，主要作用是多接觸英語，減輕對它的生疏感，鞏固以前所學過的英語，讓腦子在潛意識中吸收詞彙用法、語法結構等。

　　精讀，指小心認真地閱讀內容精彩、組織有條理、遣詞造句又正確的作品，着重點在於理解"準確"及"深入"，欣賞其精彩獨到之處。精讀時，可充分利用書中精心設計的練習，學習掌握有用的英語詞彙和語法知識。精讀後，可再花十分鐘朗讀其中一小段有趣的文字，邊唸邊細心領會文字的結構和意思。

　　《Black Cat 優質英語階梯閱讀》中的作品均值得精讀，如時間有限，不妨嘗試每兩個星期泛讀一本，輔以每星期挑選書中一章精彩的文字精讀。要學好英語，持之以恆地泛讀和精讀英文是最有效的方法。

③ 本系列的練習與測試有何功能？

　　《Black Cat 優質英語階梯閱讀》特別注重練習的設計，為讀者考慮周到，切合實用需求，學習功能強。每章後均配有訓練聽、説、讀、寫四項技能的練習，分量、難度恰到好處。

聽力練習分兩類，一是重聽故事回答問題，二是聆聽主角對話、書信朗讀、或模擬記者訪問後寫出答案，旨在以生活化的練習形式逐步提高聽力。每本書均配有 CD 提供作品朗讀，朗讀者都是專業演員，英國作品由英國演員錄音，美國作品由美國演員錄音，務求增加聆聽的真實感和感染力。多聆聽英式和美式英語兩種發音，可讓讀者熟悉二者的差異，逐漸培養分辨英美發音的能力，提高聆聽理解的準確度。此外，模仿錄音朗讀故事或模仿主人翁在戲劇中的對白，都是訓練口語能力的好方法。

閱讀理解練習形式多樣化，有縱橫字謎、配對、填空、字句重組等等，注重訓練讀者的理解、推敲和聯想等多種閱讀技能。

寫作練習尤具新意，教讀者使用網式圖示（spidergrams）記錄重點，採用問答、書信、電報、記者採訪等多樣化形式，鼓勵讀者動手寫作。

書後更設有升級測試（Exit Test）及答案，供讀者檢查學習效果。充分利用書中的練習和測試，可全面提升聽、說、讀、寫四項技能。

❹ 本系列還能提供甚麼幫助？

《Black Cat 優質英語階梯閱讀》提倡豐富多元的現代閱讀，巧用書中提供的資訊，有助於提升英語理解力，擴闊視野。

每本書都設有專章介紹相關的歷史文化知識，經典名著更有作者生平、社會背景等資訊。書內富有表現力的彩色插圖、繪圖和照片，使閱讀充滿趣味，部分加上如何解讀古典名畫的指導，增長見識。有的書還提供一些與主題相關的網址，比如關於不同國家的節慶源流的網址，讓讀者多利用網上資源增進知識。

Contents

A Note on Nathaniel Hawthorne　認識納森尼爾・霍桑　　　　9

Hawthorne and *The Scarlet Letter*　《紅字》的寫作背景　　11

CHAPTER ONE　　**The Prison Door**　牢門後的婚外情　　17

CHAPTER TWO　　**The Market Place**　在市集當眾受辱　　22

CHAPTER THREE　**The Recognition**　與丈夫相認　　38

CHAPTER FOUR　**The Encounter**　遭丈夫要脅　　48

CHAPTER FIVE　**Hester and Pearl**　與私生女相依為命　　60

CHAPTER SIX　　**The Governor's Hall**　　72
在市長大廳裏保護女兒

CHAPTER SEVEN　**The Leech and his Patient**　醫生和病者　87

CHAPTER EIGHT　**The Interior of a Heart**　內心的獨白　　99

CHAPTER NINE　**Hester and the Physician**　　111
求丈夫停止報復

CHAPTER TEN　　**The Pastor and his Parishioner**　　124
與情人重逢

CHAPTER ELEVEN　**A Flood of Sunshine**　充滿陽光的盼望　133

CHAPTER TWELVE　**The Revelation of the Scarlet Letter**　146
揭露紅字的秘密

The Puritans – the Origins　清教的起源　　32

Religion in America　美國人的不同宗教　　56

The Occult and Witchcraft　神秘學及巫術　　69

Salem and Witchcraft　老鎮塞勒姆的審巫案　　81

The Word "Witch"　何謂女巫　　97

Boston, Heart of the American Revolution　108
美國獨立戰爭發祥地——波士頓

Salem Today　　121
美麗的海濱城市和文化寶庫——今日的塞勒姆

The Importance of *The Scarlet Letter* in American Literature　157
《紅字》在美國文學史上的地位

A C T I V I T I E S　　20, 29, 44, 53, 65, 78, 94,
105, 117, 130, 141, 152

APPENDICES　**Exit Test**　　161
升級測試

Key to the Activities and Exit Test　　167
練習答案和測試答案

FCE　First Certificate in English Examination-style exercises

T: GRADE 8　Trinity-style exercises (Grade 8)

All chapters except 6 and 11 are recorded.　故事選錄

These symbols indicate the beginning and end of the extracts linked to the listening activities.　聽力練習開始和結束的標記

Nathaniel Hawthorne (1862) by Emanuel Gottlieb Leutze.

A Note on Nathaniel Hawthorne

Nathaniel Hawthorne was born on July 4, 1804, in Salem, Massachusetts, to an established New England family.

His ancestors took part in the Salem witch trials and the Quaker persecution. [1] William Hathorne (Hawthorne added the "w"), who arrived in the New World in 1630, was the judge who sentenced a Quaker woman to be whipped through the streets of Boston. His son, also a judge, presided over the notorious Salem witch trials in 1692. A woman he condemned to death during the witch trials put a curse [2] on the Hawthorne family. There is no evidence that the curse had any effect on his family. However, Nathaniel Hawthorne was aware of this curse, and it came up in his writing.

1. **persecution** : act of cruelty.
2. **curse** : a word or sentence asking God or a spirit to bring evil or harm to someone.

His ancestry explains, in part, his interest in the Puritans, and in the concepts of sin, punishment and evil.

Hawthorne decided to become a writer while at Bowdoin College in Maine. One of his classmates was Henry Wadsworth Longfellow, who later became a famous American poet.

For over a decade after graduation, he studied the Puritans and their history. In 1828, he published his first anonymous [1] novel, *Fanshawe*, which was not a success. In later life, he never mentioned this work. In 1837, he published an excellent collection of short stories, *Twice-Told Tales*.

He married Sophia Peabody in 1842, and they had three children. In 1846, he published another successful collection of short stories, *Mosses from an Old Manse*.

Salem (c. 1771) by Frederic Leizelt.

1. **anonymous** : of unknown authorship.

After leaving his employment at the Salem Customhouse in 1849, he began writing *The Scarlet Letter*, his masterpiece, which was published in 1850.

After *The Scarlet Letter*, Hawthorne published *The House of the Seven Gables* (1851) and *The Blithedale Romance* (1852). *The House of the Seven Gables* tells about a family that lives under a curse of a man condemned to death for witchcraft.

Following the election of Franklin Pierce as President of the United States in 1853, Hawthorne was appointed U.S. Consul in Liverpool and Manchester, England. After leaving this post, he traveled through Europe with his family, and lived in Italy for two years. There he wrote his last novel, *The Marble Faun* which was published in 1860 when he and his family returned to the United States.

He died away from home, on May 19th, 1864, while on a brief vacation with his friend, Franklin Pierce. He left several unfinished works.

Hawthorne and *The Scarlet Letter*

In 1976, a family living in Colorado discovered an old notebook among some papers. The notebook had been kept between 1835 and 1841 by Nathaniel Hawthorne. Like any writer's notebook, it was a collection of words, fragments [1] of sentences and ideas. It was the notebook where Hawthorne had jotted down [2] the first thoughts for his future masterpiece, *The Scarlet Letter*.

In 1838, eleven years before he began writing the novel, he had already created sketches of some of his characters. In his notes, he

1. **fragments** : parts.
2. **jotted down** : written down quickly.

wrote about "spiritual diseases and diseases of the body", and about "a sin that could cause a sore to appear on the body". The novel was taking shape in his mind. At a later date, he decided to tell the story of a woman condemned to wear the letter "A" as a sign of her adultery. [1]

Was *The Scarlet Letter* a true story? In "The Custom House", Hawthorne's introductory writing to *The Scarlet Letter*, he wrote that while working at the Customhouse in Salem, he found a mysterious package.

Inside the package he found a fine red cloth, which was worn and faded. There were traces of gold embroidery [2] on it. After examining

Boston (*c.* 1833) by William James Bennet.

1. **adultery** : voluntary sexual intercourse between a married person and somebody who is not that person's husband or wife.
2. **embroidery** : patterns, designs sewn onto material.

it carefully, he noticed that it was a capital letter "A". Each leg of the A measured exactly 3 3/4 inches (about 6 cm) in length.

There were also several sheets of faded paper in the mysterious package. They had been written long ago by Surveyor Pue, who knew the tragic story of the scarlet letter and its owner.

After further investigation, Hawthorne was able to gather more information regarding the life and sufferings of the woman who was condemned to wear the scarlet letter. The story took place in the Puritan settlement of Boston, between 1642 and 1649.

Finally in 1850, *The Scarlet Letter* was published and was immediately recognized as a classic destined to [1] fame. It has constantly remained in print ever since its first publication.

The fact that *The Scarlet Letter* involves universal themes such as love, sex, sin, evil, punishment, rebellion, hypocrisy, revenge and hate makes it a novel that cannot be forgotten by any generation.

Puritans Going to Church (1867) by George Henry Boughton.

1. **destined to** : certain to.

1 **Are these sentences true (T) or false (F)? Correct the false ones.**

		T	F
a.	A family living in Colorado discovered an old notebook with the story of *The Scarlet Letter*.	☐	☐
b.	The notebook was a collection of drawings of Hawthorne's trips abroad.	☐	☐
c.	Eleven years before Hawthorne began writing *The Scarlet Letter*, he had already created some of the characters.	☐	☐
d.	In his notes Hawthorne wrote about "spiritual diseases and diseases of the body."	☐	☐
e.	While working at the Customhouse in Salem, he found a mysterious notebook.	☐	☐
f.	The old, faded red cloth with gold embroidery was a capital letter "A".	☐	☐
g.	Surveyor Pue was the original author of *The Scarlet Letter*.	☐	☐
h.	The story is about a woman who is condemned to wear the scarlet letter in the Puritan settlement of Salem, between 1624 and 1649.	☐	☐
i.	The novel, which was published in 1850, was immediately recognized as a classic, and has constantly remained in print.	☐	☐

Before reading

1 **The concepts of love, sex, sin, evil, punishment, rebellion, hypocrisy, revenge and hate are the underlying themes of *The Scarlet Letter*. How much do you know about them?**
Choose the correct definition (1-9) and write it below. Then tick the correct box to indicate how often teenagers are involved with that feeling or action.

1. harm, badness, wickedness
2. harm done to someone in return for harm received
3. strong feeling of dislike, hostility
4. disobedience to authority
5. physical intimacy [1]
6. strong feeling of fondness or attraction
7. imposed suffering for a fault or crime
8. disobedience to God, or to religion
9. saying one thing and doing or thinking another, having two faces

Definition	Never	Sometimes	Often
a. Love:	☐	☐	☐
b. Sex:	☐	☐	☐
c. Sin:	☐	☐	☐
d. Evil:	☐	☐	☐
e. Punishment:	☐	☐	☐
f. Rebellion:	☐	☐	☐
g. Hypocrisy:	☐	☐	☐
h. Revenge:	☐	☐	☐
i. Hate:	☐	☐	☐

1. **intimacy** : closeness.

2 What other novels have you read that involve one or more of the themes in question 1?

....

....

FCE **3** Listen to Chapter 1 and choose the best answer, A, B or C.

1 The founders of the colony set aside a portion of land for a prison and a cemetery because
A. ☐ they had orders to do so.
B. ☐ they were optimists.
C. ☐ they knew there would be crime and death.

2 How old was the settlement?
A. ☐ about 15 or 20 years old
B. ☐ older than any other one in the New World
C. ☐ in June it was one year old

3 The wooden prison looked very old because
A. ☐ the door was black.
B. ☐ the oak door was broken.
C. ☐ there was rust on the door.

4 The prison was seen as
A. ☐ the oldest building in town.
B. ☐ the black flower of society.
C. ☐ an ugly weed.

5 The wild rose bush offered its beauty to
A ☐ prisoners and condemned criminals.
B ☐ people who are frail.
C ☐ the readers of the story.

Now read the text and check your answers.

CHAPTER **ONE**

The Prison Door

 A group of bearded men, in sad-colored clothes and gray steeple-crowned hats, [1] stood in front of a wooden building. Beside them stood a group of women, some wearing hoods. The heavy door of the building was made of oak, [2] covered with iron spikes. [3]

The founders of a new colony, no matter how optimistic they were, always set aside a portion of land for a cemetery, [4] and another portion for a prison. They probably built the first prison

1. **steeple-crowned hats** :
2. **oak** : type of wood.
3. **spikes** : thin, pointed pieces of metal.
4. **cemetery** : burial ground.

near Cornhill and the first burial ground on Isaac Johnson's land. It was around Johnson's grave that the old churchyard of King's Chapel grew.

Fifteen or twenty years after the settlement of the town, the wooden prison was already weatherbeaten [1] and showed the evident signs of age. The rust on the iron-work of the oak door made it look older than anything else in the New World.

In front of this sinister [2] building was a plot [3] of grass, covered with ugly weeds. [4] Evidently, there was something congenial [5] in the soil outside a prison—the black flower of civilized society— something that encouraged ugly weeds to grow.

But on one side of the entrance, there was a wild rose bush. In the month of June, it was covered with delicate, fragrant roses. They offered their fragrance and beauty to the prisoner who entered the gloomy [6] building, and to the condemned criminal who left it to meet his doom. [7]

Let us pick one of its flowers and give it to the reader.

Hopefully, this sweet flower will serve to soften the dark tones of a tale of human frailty [8] and sorrow.

END

1. **weatherbeaten** : damaged by the weather.
2. **sinister** : evil, bad.
3. **plot** : small, marked piece of ground.
4. **weeds** : unwanted wild plants or grass.
5. **congenial** : pleasant.
6. **gloomy** : dark.
7. **doom** : terrible fate, unavoidable death.
8. **frailty** : weakness.

Comprehension

1 What kind of atmosphere is created in Chapter 1?

2 What words (nouns and adjectives) are used to create this atmosphere? After you have selected them, put them in the correct list. Two examples are done for you.

Nouns	Adjectives
cemetery	sad-colored

3 What colors are predominant in this description? Why?

4 Do black flowers exist? Why is the prison described as the "black flower" of society?

Grammar

FCE 5 Use the word given to complete the second sentence, so that it has a similar meaning to the first sentence. Do not change the word given. You must use between two and five words, including the word given.

1. The women did not expect to find the men outside the prison.
    surprised
    The women .... the men outside the prison.

2. The prisoner was being followed closely.
    following
    Someone .... closely.

3. It is certain that they built the prison twenty years ago.
   must
   The prison .... twenty years ago.

4. The old oak door will need much repair work.
   have
   The old oak door .... much repair work.

5. It wasn't easy for the prisoners to stay in that gloomy building.
   difficulty
   The prisoners .... in that gloomy building.

6. Jonathan regretted going to the New World.
   wished
   Jonathan .... to the New World.

7. "Don't pick the flowers! It's not allowed," said the Puritan.
   said
   The Puritan .... the flowers because it was not allowed.

Themes for thought, discussion and writing

6 Is black considered a color of death, evil or sorrow in all societies?

7 Is white ever considered a color of death? If so, where?

8 Society often attributes colors to certain emotions, events or political tendencies. What do you attribute to these colors?

   a. red : ....
   b. pink : ....
   c. green : ....
   d. yellow : ....
   e. purple : ....
   f. black : ....
   g. white : ....
   h. blue : ....

CHAPTER **TWO**

The Market Place

On a summer morning about two centuries ago, the grass plot in front of the jail in Prison Lane was occupied by a large number of Bostonians. Their eyes were fixed on the old oak door. Their faces were grim [1] and rigid.

Every time there was such a group of people in front of the jail, there was usually a whipping of a disobedient child, a lazy bond-servant, [2] a Quaker [3] or a turbulent [4] Indian. It could also have been the hanging of a witch.

---

1. **grim** : hard, serious.
2. **bond-servant** : slave.
3. **Quaker** : see Religion in America on page 56.
4. **turbulent** : violent.

The Market Place

The spectators looked very solemn and severe, as was typical of people who believed that religion and law were almost identical.

There was practically no sympathy from the crowd for the condemned individual. What we would consider a small offense today, was then punished very harshly—even with death itself.

The women in the crowd were particularly interested in what was about to happen. They were wives and maidens [1] of English birth. Their features [2] were hard, their expressions bitter.

"Goodwives," [3] said a severe-looking woman of fifty, "we should be the ones to judge the evil doings of this Hester Prynne, since we are women of mature age and church members of good repute. [4] What do you all think? If the hussy [5] were judged by us five, would she receive the same sentence as the magistrates have decided on? I think not!"

"People say," said another woman, "that the Reverend Master Dimmesdale, her pastor, [6] is very upset that such a scandal has fallen upon his congregation."

"The magistrates are God-fearing gentlemen, but they are too generous—that is the truth," added a third older woman.

"At the very least, they should have put the brand of a hot iron on Hester Prynne's forehead. Madame Hester would have winced [7]

---

1. **maidens** : unmarried women.
2. **features** : eyes, nose, mouth and other parts of the face.
3. **Goodwives** : Puritan expression for married women.
4. **repute** : reputation.
5. **hussy** : girl or woman who behaves in an immoral way.
6. **pastor** : clergyman.
7. **winced** : moved away suddenly because of pain.

at that, I am sure! But, little will she care what they put on her dress! She could cover it with a brooch, [1] and then walk the streets as proud as ever!"

"But even if she covers the mark, the pain will always be in her heart," said a soft-spoken young wife, holding a child by hand.

"Goodness!" exclaimed a man in the crowd, "Is there no virtue [2] in a woman, except for what comes from the fear of punishment? Quiet now! The lock of the prison door is turning, and here comes Mistress Prynne herself!"

The door of the jail was thrown open, and there appeared the grim, threatening figure of the town-beadle. [3] He was like a black shadow emerging into the sunshine. He had a sword by his side and carried a staff of office. [4] His aspect represented the extreme severity of the Puritan code of law.

He stretched out the official staff in his left hand, and laid his right hand on the young woman's shoulder, pulling her forward. Once they had reached the prison door, she pushed his hand away from her shoulder. This action marked her natural dignity and force of character. She stepped out into the open air, of her own free will. In her arms, she carried an infant [5] of about three months.

When the young woman—the mother of the child—stood before the crowd, her first impulse [6] was to hold the infant close to her chest, as if to hide something that was fastened to her dress.

---

1. **brooch** : an ornament with a pin, worn on women's clothes.
2. **virtue** : goodness.
3. **town-beadle** : officer of the town.
4. **staff of office** : thick stick used as a mark of office.
5. **infant** : (here) baby.
6. **impulse** : a sudden strong desire.

After a moment, however, she realized that she was using her child, the living sign of her shame, to hide another sign of shame. Therefore, she put the child on her arm and, with a burning blush [1] and an arrogant smile, she looked straight at her townspeople. On the breast of her dress, in fine red cloth, surrounded with elaborate [2] designs in gold thread, appeared the letter "A". It was so artistically done, that it looked like a lovely decoration on her dress.

The young woman was tall, with a perfectly elegant body. She had thick, dark hair that reflected the sunshine. Her face was beautifully regular and her complexion [3] was rich in color. She had a marked brow and deep black eyes. She was lady-like, too. She had a certain gentle dignity about her. She radiated a painful, but beautiful light.

The point which drew all eyes was the SCARLET LETTER, so fantastically embroidered, [4] which illuminated [5] her. It had the effect of a spell, taking her out of the ordinary relations with humanity, and enclosing her in a sphere by herself.

---

1. **blush** : when you blush, your face becomes red because you are embarrassed.
2. **elaborate** : carefully prepared.
3. **complexion** : natural color and appearance of the skin.
4. **embroidered** : decorated.
5. **illuminated** : lightened.

The Scarlet Letter

"She is very skilled with her needle," remarked one of the female spectators, "but only a brazen [1] hussy could show her skill in this manner! This is her way of laughing at the magistrates, and making the punishment something to be proud of!"

"Oh, peace neighbors, peace!" whispered their youngest companion. "Don't let her hear you!"

"Make way, make way!" cried the beadle. "Open a passage, and I promise you that every man, woman and child will be able to look at Mistress Prynne and her apparel, [2] from now until one o'clock. A blessing on the Colony of Massachusetts, where injustice and wickedness are dragged out into the sunshine! Come along, Madame Hester, and show your scarlet letter in the marketplace!"

Hester Prynne walked towards the place of her punishment. A crowd of curious schoolboys ran in front of her, turning their heads to look at her face and at the humiliating letter on her breast. It was as though her heart had been thrown out into the street for the spectators to walk on.

However, no one could see her inner agony, and she walked serenely to the scaffold. [3] The scaffold was the platform of the pillory, [4] that horrid [5] instrument of discipline that confines the human head in its tight grip, and exposes it to the world.

Hester Prynne was not condemned to the pillory. She was condemned to stand on the scaffold, for everyone to look at. It was intolerable! The Governor, several counselors, a judge, a

---

1. **brazen** : shameless, immodest.
2. **apparel** : clothing.

3. **scaffold** :

4. **pillory** :

5. **horrid** : unpleasant.

general and the ministers of the town were all at the balcony of the meetinghouse, looking down on the platform.

As she stood on the scaffold, vivid memories of her childhood flashed through her mind. She remembered her schooldays and her years as a young girl. These memories made her forget, for a few instants, the brutal reality of the present. She remembered her native village in England and her paternal [1] home—a decayed [2] house of gray stone with a poverty-stricken [3] aspect. She saw her father's face, and her mother's too. She saw her own face, alive with the happiness and beauty of youth.

Then she remembered another face, the face of a man troubled by his years—the pale, thin face of a scholar, with dull eyes that had toiled [4] over many books. Yet, those tired eyes had a strange, penetrating power to read the human soul. Hester also remembered his slight deformity: [5] his left shoulder was a bit higher than the right.

Suddenly, Hester's mind returned to the present, to the marketplace of the Puritan settlement, with all the townspeople looking at her, at her infant and at the scarlet letter. This was her new reality.

1. **paternal** : of or like a father.
2. **decayed** : fallen to a lower or worse state, deteriorated.
3. **poverty-stricken** : extremely poor.
4. **toiled** : worked very hard for a long time.
5. **deformity** : the condition of being wrongly formed.

Comprehension

1 **Answer the following questions.**

a. Why were the townspeople gathered in front of the jail?

b. Why were the goodwives complaining? What other punishment did one goodwife suggest?

c. What was Hester's punishment?

d. Describe the memories that flashed through Hester's mind, as she stood on the scaffold.

Vocabulary

2 **Find the words in the cell window that best describe the following characters. You can use some words more than once.**

elegant body	young	dark hair	marked brow	threatening
regular face	bitter	black eyes	burning blush	hard features

colorful complexion	grim	black shadow	tall	rigid
black shadow	solemn	severe	natural dignity	arrogant smile

Hester	Women in the crowd	Spectators	Town-Beadle
....	....	....	....
....	....	....	....
....	....	....	....
....	....	....	....
....	....	....	....
....	....	....	....
....	....	....	....
....	....	....	....

Writing

3 You are a young journalist for *The Boston Gazette*. Write a newspaper article in 120-180 words about the event that just took place in front of the jail in Prison Lane on the scaffold. Use the information in the chapter and include the following details:

Part 1 – Describe the people in front of the jail.
What their comments were.

Part 2 – What happened when the jail door opened.
Describe Hester Prynne.

Part 3 – Who was present at the scaffold.
How Hester Prynne reacted to her punishment.

Start like this:

THE BOSTON GAZETTE

Yesterday on a bright summer day there was a public punishment in Boston. ....

Now find a suitable headline for your article.

Grammar

The first and second conditional

Look at these two types of "if" clauses from Chapter 2:

A *But even if she covers the mark, the pain will always be in her heart.*

This is the **first conditional** and it is used to talk about a *possible future action* or *situation*. Generally, we use the Present Simple after "if", and the future "will" after the main clause.

B *If the hussy were judged by us five, would she receive the same sentence as the magistrates have decided on?*

This is the **second conditional** and it is used to talk about an action or situation which is *improbable*, *hypothetical* or *imaginary*. Generally we use the Past Simple after "if", and "would" in the main clause.

4 Match the two parts of the sentences to make first and second conditionals.

1. ☐ If we need you urgently,   **a.** if you understand Italian.
2. ☐ If the wind continues to blow,   **b.** I would finish the book.
3. ☐ You will enjoy the opera,   **c.** you'd feel better.
4. ☐ If I had another week,   **d.** if he saw her now.
5. ☐ He would hardly recognize her,   **e.** if they plan to travel.
6. ☐ They will need a passport,   **f.** we'll call you.
7. ☐ If you got more sleep,   **g.** she will shut the window.

Themes for thought, discussion and writing

5 How does public punishment differ from private punishment? Which is more effective in your opinion?

6 Hawthorne describes the spectators as "people who believed that religion and law were almost identical." **Are there countries today where religion and law are practically the same thing? Do you think church and state should be separate? Why or why not?**

7 The human mind often protects itself from harsh, terrible events by momentarily "switching" to the past or the future, in order to block out the painful present. How did Hester's mind do this? Has this experience ever happened to you?

The Puritans – the Origins

Thomas Cranmer (1545)
by Gerlach Flicke.

Puritanism was a Protestant religious reform movement. It developed within the Church of England during the late 16th century. The Puritan movement found its origins in the writings and thinking of early religious reformers such as Thomas Cranmer, and was heavily influenced by the Protestant theologian, John Calvin whose real name was Jean Chauvin. His religious movement within Puritanism was called Calvinism. In Scotland the Calvinists became known as Presbyterians. In France they were called Huguenots.

The Puritans wanted to purify [1] the church of any remaining Roman Catholic influence. They rejected the authority of the Roman Catholic Pope and relied on the Bible as a source of religious truth. They believed in predestination: a person was either predestined by God for eternal salvation [2] or to eternal damnation. [3]

Their religious beliefs influenced every aspect of their daily life: social, political and economic. They observed austere morality, dress and behavior. They cultivated family piety, thrift, [4] honesty, business enterprise, education and science.

1. **purify** : the word Puritan comes from this word.
2. **salvation** : the state of being saved from evil and its effects.
3. **damnation** : the state of being thrown in hell.
4. **thrift** : The act of saving one's money and using it wisely.

In England they were often persecuted and they strongly desired to go to the New World where they could finally practice their religion freely, and create a settlement completely governed by Puritan ideas and laws.

In 1629 a group of Puritans and merchants convinced King Charles I of England to grant their newly formed Massachusetts Bay Company an area north of the Plymouth Colony for settlement. Initially, the company was considered a business venture, [1] but the Puritan leader, John Winthrop, decided to use the colony as a refuge [2] for persecuted Puritans.

In March 1630, Governor John Winthrop led 700 Puritans to the New World. He was on board the vessel *Arbella* followed by six other ships. The Puritans arrived in Massachusetts Bay and landed in what is now Salem. Shortly after, Governor Winthrop founded Boston, which became a prosperous seaport and the capital city.

The landing of the Pilgrims on Plymouth Rock (*c*. 1846) by Sarony & Major.

1. **venture** : a new activity involving risk.
2. **refuge** : protection from danger.

After the persecution suffered in England, they were now able to practice their stern [1] religion freely and they began to persecute their own dissenters. [2] Those who were not good members of the church were persecuted, punished and banished. If a person was accused of being a witch or a heretic, [3] he or she was burned at the stake or hanged. Blasphemy was punished very severely: the guilty person's ears were cut off!

Success in the work world was seen as a sign of God's favor, and one's predestination to salvation. In fact, shortly after their arrival, the Puritans established a flourishing fish, fur and lumber trade with many countries. Devotion to hard work and business enterprise is at the basis of the Puritan philosophy. Accumulation of wealth is not considered sinful, as long as it doesn't lead to an idle, dissolute life.

The work ethic, which is at the root of modern American society, derives from the Calvinists (Puritans). It has strongly influenced Americans from the time of the colonies to the present, even those who are not Calvinists. The work ethic has become a sort of all-encompassing American national credo. [4]

1 **Are the following sentences true (T) or false (F)? Correct the false ones.**

	T	F
a. Puritanism developed within the Roman Catholic Church, during the late 15th century.	☐	☐
b. John Calvin, the Protestant reformer, influenced the Puritan movement.	☐	☐
c. Their religious beliefs never influenced their economic and political life.	☐	☐

1. **stern** : serious, strict.
2. **dissenters** : (here) persons holding opinions different from the Puritans.
3. **heretic** : a person being guilty of holding beliefs that is against what is generally accepted.
4. **credo** : statement of beliefs and principles.

d. They wanted to go to the New World to practice their religion freely. ☐ ☐

e. The Massachusetts Bay Company was formed by King Charles I. ☐ ☐

f. In March 1630, Governor Winthrop led 700 Puritans to the New World, on board the *Arbella*. ☐ ☐

g. The Puritans landed in Boston and then founded Salem. ☐ ☐

2 **How much do you know about the Puritans? Complete the crossword puzzle, and find out!**

ACROSS	DOWN
1. inactive, indolent	**5.** the name of the ship which took Winthrop to the new world
2. the Puritans were often .... in England	
3. timber, wood	**6.** French Protestant theologian
4. what the Puritans believed in	**7.** he founded the Massachusetts Bay Colony in 1630
	8. bad language about God
	9. bad members of the church were often ....
	10. religious or dutiful behavior

3 Explain in your own words these Calvinist concepts:
   a. predestination
   b. the work ethic

4 In the United States, the Calvinist concept of the work ethic has grown and developed very strongly in all sectors of society. It is believed that with hard work, thrift and honesty, anyone can achieve success.

What are the advantages and disadvantages of this way of thinking? Fill in the table below.

Advantages	Disadvantages

5 Compare tables with your friends and discuss them.

6 Do you agree with the Calvinist work ethic? Why or why not?

7 How important is success in the work world to you?

☐ extremely important   ☐ quite important
☐ very important   ☐ not important

8 Arrange the following in order of their importance to you with 1 as most important and 3 as least important.

☐ family   ☐ free time   ☐ work

Before reading

FCE **1** **Listen to the first part of Chapter Three and choose the best answer, A, B or C.**

1   Whom did Hester see while she was on the platform?

A ☐   curious schoolboys
B ☐   the town-beadle
C ☐   a white man

2   Who had been a prisoner of the Indians?

A ☐   Master Dimmesdale
B ☐   the stranger
C ☐   the town-beadle

3   What was the usual penalty for Hester's crime?

A ☐   death
B ☐   exile
C ☐   the scaffold

4   What upset the stranger?

A ☐   That Hester was on the scaffold.
B ☐   That the child was on the scaffold with her.
C ☐   That the partner of Hester's shame was not known.

5   Who had assembled at the meetinghouse to discuss the case?

A ☐   the stranger and Master Dimmesdale
B ☐   several important men of authority and religion
C ☐   the people of Boston

CHAPTER **THREE**

The Recognition

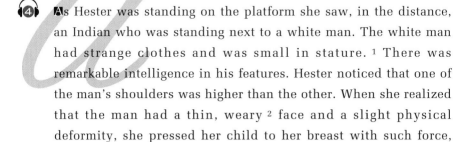

As Hester was standing on the platform she saw, in the distance, an Indian who was standing next to a white man. The white man had strange clothes and was small in stature. [1] There was remarkable intelligence in his features. Hester noticed that one of the man's shoulders was higher than the other. When she realized that the man had a thin, weary [2] face and a slight physical deformity, she pressed her child to her breast with such force, that the poor infant cried out.

The stranger had set his eyes on Hester. At first, he looked at her carelessly. But after a while, his look became intense and

1. **stature** : natural height of the body.
2. **weary** : exhausted.

38

penetrating. Then, a look of horror crossed his face. He tried to control his strong emotions, and soon he appeared to be calm.

At this point, he met Hester's eyes. She appeared to recognize him. He slowly raised his finger, and put it on his lips.

He then asked a townsman the following question. "Who is this woman and why is she on the platform?"

"You must be a stranger in this area, my friend," answered the townsman, looking curiously at the man and his Indian companion, "otherwise you would have heard of Mistress Hester Prynne and her evil doings. She has created a scandal in Master Dimmesdale's church."

"Really?" said the man. "I am a stranger. I have traveled by land and sea, and I have been a prisoner of the Indians. Please tell me of this woman's offenses."

"That woman, sir, was the wife of a well-educated man, English by birth, who had lived in Amsterdam for a long time. One day he decided to settle in Massachusetts. Therefore, he sent his wife first, and he remained in Amsterdam to look after some business. Two years have passed, and the young woman has never received any news from her husband."

"I understand," replied the stranger. "And who is the father of the infant?"

"The matter is a mystery. Madame Hester refuses to speak. Our Massachusetts magistrates have been merciful [1] with Hester Prynne. They say that she is young and fair, [2] and was strongly tempted to her fall. Moreover, it is likely that her husband may be at the bottom of the sea. If the magistrates had followed the law to

1. **merciful** : willing to forgive instead of punishing.
2. **fair** : (here) very attractive, beautiful.

its extreme, the penalty would have been death! Instead, the penalty is to stand on the platform for three hours. And then, to wear the mark of shame on her breast for the rest of her life."

"A wise sentence," said the stranger. "She will be a living sermon [1] against sin until the shameful letter is engraved [2] on her tombstone. It upsets me that the partner of her shame is not standing on the platform by her side. But he will be known!—he will be known!—he will be known!"

He bowed courteously to the townsman and left the crowd with his Indian companion.

Hester stood on the scaffold, staring at the stranger. In her heart she was thankful that the crowd, dreadful in itself, was there to separate her from him—to protect her from him! She dreaded the moment when she would have to meet him alone, face to face.

Several important men of authority and religion had assembled at the meetinghouse to discuss and judge Hester Prynne's case. These older men were, without doubt, good, wise, just and virtuous. But they were not capable of judging the good and evil in a woman's heart.

END

Governor Bellingham, head of the community, was present. The famous Reverend John Wilson, the oldest clergyman in Boston, called out Hester's name.

"Hester Prynne," said the clergyman, "I have tried to persuade my young brother, Reverend Dimmesdale, to deal with you in discussing the vileness [3] of your sin. Reverend Dimmesdale is

---

1. **sermon** : long talk about moral matters or about somebody's faults.
2. **engraved** : cut on wood, stone, metal.
3. **vileness** : wickedness, evil.

The Recognition

your pastor and knows you better than I. Hester Prynne, you must not continue to hide the name of he who tempted you to this grievous [1] fall.

"Reverend Dimmesdale does not agree with me. He feels that it is against the nature of a woman to force her to open the secrets of her heart to the world. Who will deal with this poor sinner's soul?"

There was a murmur among the dignified occupants of the balcony.

Governor Bellingham spoke in an authoritative voice, "Master Dimmesdale, the responsibility of this woman's soul is yours. You must convince her to repent [2] and confess."

The whole crowd looked at Reverend Dimmesdale, a young clergyman, who had come from the great English universities, bringing all his learning to the wilderness. [3] He was eloquent [4] and deeply religious. He had a striking aspect with large, brown, melancholy [5] eyes, and a mouth which tended to tremble. This expressed both nervous sensibility and a great power of self-control. The young minister had a worried, almost frightened look. He was simple and childlike, but his sermons, which reflected his purity of thought, affected his listeners like the speech of an angel.

"Speak to the woman, my brother," said Mr Wilson. "She must confess the truth!"

1. **grievous** : seriously harmful.
2. **repent** : be sorry for wrongdoing.
3. **wilderness** : area of wild uncultivated land.
4. **eloquent** : able to speak well and influence listeners.
5. **melancholy** : very sad.

The Scarlet Letter

"Hester Prynne," said Reverend Dimmesdale, leaning over the balcony and looking into her eyes, "you have heard what Reverend Wilson said. I ask you to confess the name of your fellow sinner. Do not have pity for him. Your silence will not save his soul. Your silence will only make him add hypocrisy to sin. It is better for him to join you on the platform than to hide a guilty heart all through his life."

The young pastor's voice was sweet, rich, deep and broken. He was able to evoke sympathy from the crowd.

Hester shook her head.

"Woman, do not go beyond the limits of Heaven's mercy!" cried Reverend Wilson. "Speak out the name! That name and your repentance could help to take the scarlet letter off your breast."

"Never!" replied Hester, looking into the deep and troubled eyes of Reverend Dimmesdale.

"Speak, woman!" said another stern voice from the crowd. "Speak and give your child a father!"

"I will not speak!" answered Hester, turning as pale as death.

"She will not speak," murmured Reverend Dimmesdale, who was leaning over the balcony with his hand on his heart. He moved back with a long sigh. "What strength and generosity in a woman's heart. She will not speak!"

Comprehension

FCE ❶ **Choose the answer, A, B, C or D, which you think fits best according to the text.**

1. Where did Hester's husband live for a long time?
   A ☐ England
   B ☐ Amsterdam
   C ☐ Massachusetts
   D ☐ With the Indians

2. Why were the magistrates merciful with Hester?
   A ☐ Because she was educated.
   B ☐ Because she had a young child.
   C ☐ Because she was young and fair.
   D ☐ Because she was very ill.

3. Why were several important men of authority and religion assembled at the meetinghouse?
   A ☐ to punish Hester
   B ☐ to discuss and judge Hester's case
   C ☐ to speak with the stranger
   D ☐ to discuss the problem of the Indians

4. Who was responsible for Hester's soul?
   A ☐ Reverend Dimmesdale
   B ☐ Reverend Wilson
   C ☐ Governor Bellingham
   D ☐ the stranger

5. Reverend Dimmesdale was young,
   A ☐ shy and afraid.
   B ☐ happy and friendly.
   C ☐ silent and mysterious.
   D ☐ eloquent and deeply religious.

6. What did Hester refuse to do?
   A ☐ She refused to wear the scarlet letter A.
   B ☐ She refused to speak to Reverend Dimmesdale.
   C ☐ She refused to reveal the name of her fellow sinner.
   D ☐ She refused to reveal the name of her child.

FCE ② Who said what?

Look back at Chapter Three and for questions 1-12 choose from the people (A-F).

A = Hester Prynne

B = the stranger

C = the townsman

D = Reverend John Wilson

E = Governor Bellingham

F = Reverend Dimmesdale

"Speak out the name!"	**1.**	....
"You must be a stranger in this area."	**2.**	....
"Hester Prynne, you must not continue to hide the name of he who tempted you to this grievous fall."	**3.**	....
"Master Dimmesdale... you must convince her to repent and confess."	**4.**	....
"The matter is a mystery."	**5.**	....
"Your silence will not save his soul."	**6.**	....
"I will not speak!"	**7.**	....
"Do not go beyond the limits of Heaven's mercy."	**8.**	....
"Your silence will only make him add hypocrisy to sin."	**9.**	....
"Never!"	**10.**	....
"She will be a living sermon against sin until the shameful letter is engraved on her tombstone."	**11.**	....
"What strength and generosity in a woman's heart!"	**12.**	....

Grammar

Relative clauses

Look at these sentences:

*The building **which** frightened her was the dark prison.*
*She saw an Indian **who** was standing next to a white man.*

"Which" and "who" are the subject of the verb in the relative clause and cannot be omitted.

Now look at these sentences:

*The Indian **(who)** he spoke to yesterday is a friend.*
*The evil doings **(which)** he mentioned were true.*

"Who" and "which" are the object of the verb and can be omitted.

3 **Look at this dialogue between a stranger and a Puritan of Boston. Decide whether *who* or *which* are needed, and circle the correct word in the brackets.**

Stranger: Who is the young woman on the scaffold?

Puritan: She is a woman 1 *(who, which, omit)* came from Amsterdam. She is the one 2 *(who, which, omit)* has greatly upset Reverend Dimmesdale's congregation.

Stranger: What has she done?

Puritan: Oh, the sin 3 *(who, which, omit)* stains her soul is a terrible one. The sin 4 *(who, which, omit)* she committed is difficult to pronounce. A woman 5 *(who, which, omit)* commits such a sin is evil.

Stranger: What is it?

Puritan: It is a sin 6 *(who, which, omit)* we Puritans punish severely. It is adultery! Reverend Dimmesdale, a holy man 7 *(who, which, omit)* has studied in England, is deeply bothered by the sin 8 *(who, which, omit)* I have just mentioned.

Before reading

FCE ❶ **Listen to the first part of Chapter Four and choose the best answer, A, B or C.**

1. When Hester returned to prison, she was
   A ☐ sleepy.
   B ☐ angry.
   C ☐ nervous.

2. The physician was staying in the prison because
   A ☐ he was Master Brackett's friend.
   B ☐ he was a guest.
   C ☐ he was a prisoner.

3. The physician gave the medicine to the child
   A ☐ who stopped crying and fell asleep.
   B ☐ who became very ill.
   C ☐ who died.

4. The physician gave Hester
   A ☐ nothing to drink.
   B ☐ an old Indian medicine.
   C ☐ a cup of water.

5. Hester was the physician's
   A ☐ sister.
   B ☐ daughter.
   C ☐ wife.

CHAPTER **FOUR**

The Encounter

After her return to prison, Hester Prynne was in a state of nervous excitement. It was impossible for her to remain calm. The infant was not feeling well either. It was crying desperately and was obviously in pain.

Master Brackett, the jailer, decided to call a physician, [1] who was staying in the prison as a guest until the magistrates could meet with the Indians to decide his ransom. [2] The physician's name was Roger Chillingworth. The jailer accompanied him to Hester's cell. When she saw the man that she had noticed in the crowd, she became as still as death.

---

1. **physician** : doctor.
2. **ransom** : sum of money paid to free a prisoner.

The Encounter

The physician entered the room quietly and examined the infant carefully. He then opened his leather case and took out a medicine that he mixed with water.

"Here, woman! The child is yours—she is not mine. Make the child drink from this cup."

Hester refused the medicine, and at the same time gazed at him with apprehension. [1] "Would you avenge [2] yourself on this innocent child?" she whispered.

"Foolish woman!" responded the physician. "Why should I harm this suffering child? The medicine is good and strong, and if it were my child, I would give it."

Hester still hesitated, so he took the infant and gave it the medicine. The child stopped crying after a while, and then fell asleep.

The physician proceeded to examine the mother, and then prepared another medicine for her.

"Drink this! It is an old Indian medicine. It will calm you but it cannot give you a sinless conscience. I have no medicine for that."

"Is there death in this cup?" Hester asked.

"Do you know me so little, Hester Prynne? If I want revenge, what better revenge than to let you live, so that your shame can always be on your bosom?" He touched the scarlet letter with his long finger.

"Live, therefore, and support your punishment in the eyes of men and women, in the eyes of your husband, in the eyes of your child."

Hester drank the medicine and sat down on the bed where the child was sleeping. The physician sat down near the bed. Hester

1. **apprehension** : anxiety, fear.
2. **avenge** : revenge.

The Scarlet Letter

knew that she had deeply and irreparably [1] injured the man who sat next to her.

"It was my folly, [2] my weakness, to marry you," said the physician. "I was a man in decay, [3] having given my best years to feed my dream of knowledge. I was born with a physical deformity. Why did I ever think that my intellectual gifts could compensate for my misshapen [4] body and my age in the eyes of a beautiful, young girl!

"From the moment when we came down the church steps together, as husband and wife, I should have known that there would be a scarlet letter at the end of our path."

END

"You knew that I did not love you. I never pretended to love you. I have always been frank with you," said Hester.

"True," he replied. "It was my folly. In my life, the world has been a cheerless place. My heart was sad and lonely without a household fire. I was looking for a little happiness, a little warmth. And so, Hester, I took you into my heart."

"I have greatly wronged [5] you," murmured Hester.

"We have wronged each other," answered the physician. "By marrying you, I created an unnatural relation between your youth and my decay. I plan no vengeance [6] against you, Hester. Between you and me the scale hangs fairly balanced. But who is the man who has wronged us both?"

---

1. **irreparably** : fatally.
2. **folly** : foolishness, stupidity.
3. **decay** : deterioration.
4. **misshapen** : deformed.
5. **wronged** : treated in an unfair way.
6. **vengeance** : revenge.

The Scarlet Letter

"Do not ask me! You will never know!" replied Hester vehemently. [1]

"Never? Believe me, Hester, there are very few things hidden from the man who devotes himself to solving a mystery. All my life, I have searched for the truth in books. I will search for him and I will find him! Sooner or later, he must be mine!"

The eyes of the wrinkled scholar glowed so intensely upon her, that Hester put her hands over her heart, fearing that he might read her secret.

"You will not reveal his name, but he is mine. He does not wear a scarlet letter, but I will read it on his heart. He will be mine!"

Hester was terrified.

"You have kept the secret of your lover's name. Now, keep my secret! No one here knows me. Do not tell a soul that I am your husband. I will pitch [2] my tent here where I have ties — a woman, a man and a child. No matter whether my ties are of love or hate. You, Hester Prynne, belong to me. My home is where you are and where he is. But do not betray me!"

"Why not announce yourself openly and cast me off?" [3] Hester asked.

"It may be that I do not want the dishonor of being the husband of a faithless woman. It may be for other reasons. Let everyone think that I am dead. If you betray me, beware! His fame, his position, his life will be in my hands. Beware!"

"I will keep your secret, as I have kept his," said Hester.

"Swear it!" he insisted. And she swore.

---

1. **vehemently** : fiercely; in strong opposition to something.
2. **pitch** : set up.
3. **cast me off** : reject, abandon me.

Comprehension

1 **Answer the following questions.**

a. Why was it impossible for Hester to remain calm?

b. What was the physician doing in the prison?

c. Why was Hester afraid of the physician's medicine?

d. How did the infant react to the medicine?

e. Had Hester loved Chillingworth in the past?

f. Why did Chillingworth say, "Between you and me the scale hangs fairly balanced"?

g. How did Chillingworth plan to discover Hester's lover?

h. Why didn't Chillingworth announce himself openly and reject Hester?

i. What secret must Hester keep?

FCE 2 **Read the summary of Chapters One to Four and think of the word which best fits each space. Use only *one* word for each space.**

In Puritan Boston Hester Prynne was accused (**1**) .... adultery and the leading men of the Puritan settlement met (**2**) .... decide her punishment. It was decided that Hester (**3**) .... stand (**4**) .... the platform (**5**) .... three hours where everyone could see her. Then, she was condemned to wear a scarlet "A" on the breast of (**6**) .... dress all her life. The Puritan leaders asked her to reveal the name of her lover but she refused. While she and her infant were in prison, her husband, Roger Chillingworth, (**7**) .... was a physician, went to speak to her. He was determined to (**8**) .... Hester's lover, although he planned no revenge (**9**) .... Hester. She swore to keep (**10**) .... real identity a secret.

Grammar

Non-defining relative clauses

Look at this example from Chapter 4:

Master Brackett, the jailer, decided to call a physician, **who was staying in prison as a guest until the magistrates could meet with the Indians to decide a ransom.**

In the example, the man is identified, he is a physician, so the relative clause *doesn't identify him*. It simply gives us *extra information* about him. Look at these examples:

The prison, **which was built 20 years ago,** *was a sinister building.*
The jailer, **who was also a friend of the governor,** *spoke to them.*

We use *non-defining relative clauses* to give *extra information* about the person or thing we are talking about.
***Non-defining relative clauses* must be introduced by a relative pronoun such as *who, which, whose*.**

Remember!
With non-defining relative clauses:
* **we cannot use *that***
* **we usually separate them from the main clause by a comma, or by two commas**

③ Join the sentences below using *who, which* or *whose*.

   a. Hester Prynne is a new member of the community. She has just arrived from Amsterdam.

   b. Boston is on the Atlantic coast. It is one of America's leading cities.

   c. Reverend Dimmesdale became the most respected reverend of the settlement. His behavior was ambiguous.

   d. Nathaniel Hawthorne is considered one of America's greatest writers. He died in 1864.

   e. The new school will open in September. It is three miles away.

   f. The young man is the new governor of Boston. His sister is a teacher in Salem.

Themes for thought, discussion and writing

4 **Do you think Roger Chillingworth is a reasonable, objective man? Why?/Why not?**

5 **Chillingworth says,** "I will pitch my tent here where I have ties — a woman, a man and a child. No matter whether my ties are of love or hate." **The human emotions of love and hate are very different — they are opposites. Yet both love and hate are intense emotions that involve the heart and mind of an individual. In this respect, they are very similar because they can create a certain pattern of action and reaction. The real "opposite" of love and hate is indifference.**

A   **Name a thing or a person that:**
- **you love**
- **you hate**
- **is indifferent to you**

B   **How do you react to each of these?**

T: GRADE 8

6 **TOPIC – SOCIETY**
Today's society is quite different from the Puritanical one of *The Scarlet Letter*. Discuss the following points:

a. In what ways has society changed?

b. Is this the case for societies in all countries?

c. What do you think some of the advantages of such a society were/are?

d. If you had been in Hester's situation in 17th century Boston, would you have reacted differently? If so, explain how.

Religion in America

Nearly every religion in the world is represented in the United States, although Christianity predominates. [1] All religions are protected in their worship by the Bill of Rights and by a long tradition of separation of Church and State. The U.S. Constitution forbids the establishment of a national religion. Today approximately 40% of the nation's population attends religious services on a weekly basis.

Among the first white men in America were Spanish Roman Catholic missionaries who, beginning in the early 16th century, went to the southwest to convert Indians to Christianity.

The Puritans who settled New England in the early 17th century had left England to practice their strict religion freely. Roger Williams, a Salem minister, was banished from the Massachusetts Bay Colony because of a difference of opinion with his fellow Puritans. He founded Rhode Island in 1636, and it became the first American colony to allow religious freedom.

The Church of England was firmly established in Virginia after 1619. The southeast states attracted several Protestant religions: Methodists, Baptists, Presbyterians and Huguenots.

Maryland was founded as a refuge for English Catholics. New York and New Jersey were centers of the Dutch Reformed Church. In 1654, twenty-three Portuguese Jews settled in New York. Four years later, a community of Jews arrived in Rhode Island.

The Quakers, or Society of Friends, was another religious group, inspired by the Protestant Reformation. The Quakers believed that the purpose of life was to worship God and to suffer voluntarily. They

1. **predominates** : having the main power or influence.

American methodists proceeding to their camp meeting (c. 1819)
by Jaques Gérard Milbert.

believed that they could approach God directly, without the clergy. This belief and their stern lifestyle made them very unpopular. They were persecuted in England and in the New World. The Quakers were finally able to live freely in Pennsylvania which welcomed other radical Christian groups, particularly from Germany. These included the Amish, Mennonites, Dunkards and Moravians.

Today about 70,000 Amish practice their religion in about 50 communities in the United States and Canada. They live as simply as possible, avoiding all modern conveniences such as electricity and automobiles. They speak Amish among themselves and dress like they did long ago.

After 1831, there was the rise of the Mormon religion. Their beliefs and practices set them apart (for example, they practice polygamy [1]) and they were driven away from Ohio, Missouri and Illinois. Finally, they settled in Utah, which today is a predominantly Mormon state.

Other religions that are active in America are the Eastern Orthodox, Jehovah's Witnesses, Seventh-Day Adventists, Moslems, Hindus and Buddhists. There are also numerous sects, [2] which seem to spring up [3] frequently.

Great progress has been made towards religious freedom in the United States over the past four hundred years.

Temple Square, Salt Lake City (c. 1899) by William Henry Jackson.

1. **polygamy** : custom of having more than one wife at the same time.
2. **sects** : groups of people who share beliefs or opinions.
3. **spring up** : appear suddenly.

1 Fill in the gaps with the words from the box.

> Puritan   missionaries   Amish   Spanish
> Pennsylvania   accepted   banished   Salem
> Maryland   Mormons   Christian   Rhode Island

a. In the United States, the .... religion predominates.

b. The first white settlers in America were ....
Catholic ....

c. Roger Williams was a .... minister who lived
in ....

d. Williams was .... and later founded
.............................., where all religions were ....

e. English Catholics found refuge in ....

f. The Quakers settled in ....

g. The .... avoid all modern conveniences.

h. Utah was settled mainly by ....

Before reading

FCE 1 Listen to the first part of Chapter Five and complete the
sentences below.

Hester was alone in the world   1 ....

When she died,   2 ....

Hester was free   3 ....

The father of the child   4 ....

Hester and her child lived   5 ....

Hester was skilled   6 ....

She often gave   7 ....

CHAPTER FIVE

Hester and Pearl

Hester Prynne's prison term was over. The prison door was thrown open, and she came out into the bright sunshine. For Hester's tormented [1] heart, the sunshine had no other purpose than to reveal the scarlet letter on her breast.

From this day on, she would be alone in the world with her shame. And each day would be the same, as her burden of shame, misery and solitude [2] grew heavier and harder to bear. Even after her death, her grave would bear the sign of her sin, of her shame.

Hester, however, was free to leave the Puritan settlement of Boston. She was free to return to her birthplace or to any other European land, where she could begin a new life. But there is a strange fatality [3] that attracts human beings irresistibly to the

1. **tormented** : painful.
2. **solitude** : loneliness.
3. **fatality** : deadliness.

place where a great event has given color and perhaps meaning to their lives. And it seems that the more tragic the event, the greater the attraction to that place.

Her sin, her ignominy, [1] were the roots that she had planted in the soil of the Puritan settlement. Perhaps another feeling kept her there too; a feeling that she was afraid to recognize, a feeling that she hid from herself. In the Puritan settlement, there lived the man who was her partner in sin and the father of her child.

She forced herself to believe that the reason for remaining in New England was that here, she would purge her soul through humiliation, shame and suffering.

Therefore, Hester did not flee. She and her child went to live in a small thatched [2] cottage near the seashore and far from the Puritan settlement. She lived a life of isolation. She had no friends.

Her only contact with other humans was through her work. She possessed an art that was required even in these barren [3] lands — the art of needle work. She was exceptionally skilled with the needle.

Public ceremonies, installation of magistrates, funeral robes and baby linen all required rich embroidery and beautiful ornamentation. [4] Hester had a good amount of work to do all year long. But never was she called to embroider the white veil of a young bride. This indicated the relentless [5] vigor [6] with which society punished her for her sin.

---

1. **ignominy** : disgrace, dishonor, humiliation.
2. **thatched** : (roof) made of dried straw, reeds, etc.
3. **barren** : empty, dry.
4. **ornamentation** : decoration.
5. **relentless** : persistent, inflexible.
6. **vigor** : strength of thought.

The Scarlet Letter

Hester often gave contributions to charity to help the poor of the community. She made clothes for them too. The poor often scorned [1] her, but they readily accepted her charity.

END

Hester felt completely excluded from society. Every gesture, every word, and even the silence of those she contacted expressed that she was banished. [2]

If she entered a church on the Sabbath, she was immediately the object of gossip and scorn. Hester began to fear children for when she walked through the town they followed her, screaming insults.

Terrible legends grew around the scarlet letter. Some people believed that it was red-hot with infernal [3] fire, and could be seen glowing at night when Hester walked outside.

Hester had named her little girl Pearl because a pearl was an object of great price. And she had paid a very high price indeed for her Pearl.

Hester knew that what she had done was evil, and she believed that its result would not be good. Therefore, she fearfully examined Pearl, expecting to discover something dark, peculiar or perverse [4] in the child.

Pearl had no physical defect. She had an inborn grace that accompanied her flawless [5] beauty. In this little girl, there was something both wild and majestic. [6]

---

1. **scorned** : treated with anger and disrespect.
2. **banished** : sent away.
3. **infernal** : hellish.
4. **perverse** : strange.
5. **flawless** : perfect.
6. **majestic** : beautiful and causing admiration.

The Scarlet Letter

Hester made her richly decorated dresses that enhanced Pearl's beauty. She did everything in her power to be a strict, but loving mother.

As Pearl grew, Hester could not help asking herself if she was a human child. Her shiny black eyes had a look that was very intelligent, yet inexplicable, [1] perverse and sometimes malicious. [2] She was an enigma [3] for her mother. For the townspeople, Pearl was a demon [4] offspring [5] — a living sin!

The first thing Pearl noticed in her life was the scarlet letter on Hester's breast. She would grab it with her little hand and then she would look into her mother's eyes with a peculiar smile. This peculiar smile puzzled and frightened Hester.

Pearl was an outcast [6] in the children's world. She was considered a product of sin, an evil child that had no right to be with the other children of the Puritan community of Boston.

---

1. **inexplicable** : unable to be understood.
2. **malicious** : intended to harm other people.
3. **enigma** : mystery.
4. **demon** : an evil spirit.
5. **offspring** : child.
6. **outcast** : person who is rejected by his or her social group.

Comprehension

FCE ❶ Read the text below and decide which answer, A, B, C or D, best fits each space.

When Hester's prison (**1**) .... was over she was free to go (**2**) .... she wanted. But she (**3**) .... to remain in the Puritan settlement. Hester was very (**4**) .... with the needle and she had (**5**) .... of work to do.

(**6**) .... was her friend and she lived in complete isolation with little Pearl. Horrible legends grew (**7**) .... the scarlet letter. Hester often examined Pearl (**8**) .... to find something strange or peculiar in the child. Hester (**9**) .... Pearl beautifully decorated dresses but she did (**10**) .... to be a strict mother.

1. A days	**B** period	**C** term	**D** time
2. A anywhere	**B** everywhere	**C** nowhere	**D** out
3. A determined	**B** decided	**C** believed	**D** reasoned
4. A smart	**B** great	**C** able	**D** skilled
5. A lots	**B** many	**C** amount	**D** always
6. A No	**B** Anybody	**C** Nobody	**D** None
7. A about	**B** around	**C** referring	**D** on
8. A going	**B** awaiting	**C** assuming	**D** expecting
9. A made	**B** built	**C** did	**D** created
10. A every	**B** anything	**C** everything	**D** all

FCE ❷ Use the word given to complete the second sentence, so that it has a similar meaning to the first sentence. Do not change the word given. You must use between two and five words, including the word given.

1. The townspeople did not let Pearl enter the school.
allowed
Pearl .... to enter the school.

2. The heavy rains caused serious floods in Boston.
brought
Serious floods .... by the heavy rains.

3. The poor scorned Hester although she always helped them.
   spite
   The poor scorned Hester .... help.

4. Hester offered a gift to the governor but he did not accept it.
   turned
   The governor .... gift.

5. The townspeople said Pearl was a living sin.
   accused
   Pearl .... a living sin.

6. Although it looks easy, embroidery is very difficult.
   not
   Embroidery .... as it looks.

7. The Reverend had received a bad injury to his hand.
   was
   The Reverend's .... injured.

Grammar

Phrasal verbs

Look at this sentence from Chapter 5:

*The prison door was thrown open, and she **came out into** the bright sunshine.*

***Came out into** is a phrasal verb. Phrasal verbs are an important part of the English language. A phrasal verb is a combination of a verb and an adverb or preposition. Normally, the usual meaning of the verb is changed.*

Look at this example and discover another meaning of *came out into*:

*The inspector **came out into** the open with the story of the company's bankruptcy.*

3 **A Match the phrasal verb with the correct definition.**

1. ☐ come out of one's ears
2. ☐ come out in the wash
3. ☐ come out on top
4. ☐ come out badly
5. ☐ come out at someone or something
6. ☐ come out of the blue

a. to have a bad result

b. to end up being the winner

c. to emerge and attack someone or something

d. to be very abundant

e. to appear or be revealed suddenly

f. (for a problem) to be solved or to fade away

B Now fill in the gaps with the appropriate phrasal verb in its correct form.

a. As we crossed the park, the dogs .... us, but we got away.

b. It will take time to solve this problem, but in the end it will ....

c. I turned the corner and I was very surprised to see David ....

d. The new restaurant is very successful. It has clients ....

e. The volleyball team worked hard all year, and it ....

f. At the meeting everyone was shouting and screaming. I was sorry that it ....

Themes for thought, discussion and writing

4 In addition to Hester's "official" punishment, the Puritan society punished her and Pearl relentlessly in many ways, through silence, isolation, exclusion, scorn and discrimination. Which of these forms of "indirect" punishment do you think causes more suffering? Why?

5 Hawthorne writes, "Every gesture... expressed that she was banished." Gestures, conscious or subconscious, are part of a person's body language. Body language should be observed and "listened to" because it often says more than words. Have you ever been in a situation where a person said one thing, but his or her body language expressed something entirely different?

6 Hester was free to leave Boston, but she chose to stay. Hawthorne writes that human beings are irresistibly attracted to the place where a "great event has given color and perhaps meaning to their lives." This is very true with criminals, who return again and again to the scene of the crime. This has been a recurring theme in many novels, such as Fyodor Dostoevsky's *Crime and Punishment*.

Why do you think human beings are like this? Could it be the heart overruling the brain? Or could it be the subconscious desire to get caught and "pay" for the crime?

Writing

7 Imagine you are Hester and that you are writing to your mother and father in England to tell them about what has happened to you. Include the following points:
  - her punishment on the scaffold and the scarlet letter
  - her meeting with the leading men of Boston
  - her isolated life in Boston
  - her daughter Pearl

Write your letter in 120-180 words. Start like this:

Dear Mother and Father.
Many things have happened since I last wrote you ....

The Occult and Witchcraft

People have always been fascinated by the occult: beliefs about a mysterious "other world", hidden forces around them, secret sources of knowledge, and latent [1] powers within themselves. Some individuals feel they have supernatural powers or occult powers that they can use to contact the "other world", to make good or bad things happen, to cast spells, or to predict future events.

Occult lore [2] is less concerned with explaining events than with trying to predict, stop or induce [3] them. Linked to this lore is the belief in life after death, and in spirits and ghosts.

De Proprietatibus rerum (15th century) by Barthélemy l'Anglais, depicting the Zodiac.

1. **latent** : existing but not yet active or visible.
2. **lore** : traditional knowledge on a particular subject.
3. **induce** : cause something to happen.

The ancient Babylonians and Egyptians were great believers in the occult. Astrology originated in Babylonia about three thousand years ago. The Babylonians believed that they could predict the future by interpreting the positions of the sun, moon and planets.

The ancient Egyptians and Greeks also studied the heavenly bodies. They drew maps of the sky showing named constellations. The Greek zodiac is the one we still use today.

Pagan cults based on occult rituals survived the growth of such major religions as Christianity. But after the 14th century, occult practices began to be condemned by the Church as evil or satanic. There was growing persecution of sects [1] that believed that the material world was created by the devil. People accused of devil worship or Satanic rites were persecuted, tortured and burned at the stake. [2] This was the beginning of the witch hunts which took place throughout Europe and America until the 18th century.

It was believed that witches were in contact with the devil and other evil spirits. This gave them magic powers to cast spells and curses on people, and to make bad things happen.

Prayers, rituals and talismans were used to ward off [3] evil spirits and bad luck. Some folk superstitions remain today, such as touching wood, or carrying a good luck charm.

Exorcism is still used today to "drive the devil out" of a person who is said to be possessed by Satan.

Prophecy, fortune-telling, palmistry, astrology and tarot cards are just some of the things that are still present in our modern society.

All over the world today, there are people who believe in magic and the occult and who perform Satanic rites. Witchcraft is often called "black magic".

1. **sects** : groups of people who share beliefs which different from those of most people.
2. **burned at the stake** : killed someone by tying them to a post and burning them.
3. **ward off** : keep away.

Witchcraft will probably never die because it satisfies the need of some people to predict, influence or control the mysteries of life.

1 **Choose the correct answer.**

1. A definition of the occult is
   A ☐ having to do with secret, mysterious, or supernatural beliefs, events and predictions.
   B ☐ having to do with life after death.
   C ☐ another name for early Christian rituals.

2. Spirits and ghosts are
   A ☐ created by the devil.
   B ☐ worshipped by certain cults.
   C ☐ part of the occult lore.

3. Pagan cults were based on
   A ☐ the worship of nature.
   B ☐ occult rituals.
   C ☐ early Christian beliefs.

4. After the 14th century, the Christian Church
   A ☐ persecuted and executed witches.
   B ☐ tried to convert devil worshippers.
   C ☐ banished witches to the forest.

5. It was believed that witches were in contact with Satan, and
   A ☐ lived forever.
   B ☐ could "drive the devil out" of a person.
   C ☐ had magic powers to cast spells, curses, and make bad things happen.

6. Witchcraft
   A ☐ ended in the 18th century.
   B ☐ is still practiced today.
   C ☐ is only practiced in primitive societies.

CHAPTER SIX

The Governor's Hall

One day, Hester went to Governor Bellingham's mansion to return a pair of gloves that he had given her to embroider. She had decided to return the embroidered gloves, and talk to him regarding certain gossip that she had recently heard. The townspeople had been saying that Governor Bellingham and other leading citizens wanted to take Pearl away from her mother since she was considered a lowly sinner, and could not possibly raise her child in a Christian way. *If the child was really capable of moral and religious growth, and possessed the elements of salvation, then she would be better off away from her mother.* Hester, therefore, was determined to talk to the governor and convince him to let her keep Pearl.

The Governor's Hall

For this occasion, Pearl was wearing a crimson [1] velvet dress, abundantly embroidered with gold thread. Pearl possessed a rich and luxuriant beauty. There was a fire in her; she seemed the unpremeditated offshoot [2] of a passionate moment.

The child's appearance was an inevitable reminder of what Hester was condemned to wear on her bosom. [3] Pearl was the scarlet letter in another form — the living scarlet letter!

They reached the governor's mansion and a bond-servant opened the door.

"Is Governor Bellingham in?" inquired Hester.

"Yes, he is," replied the bond-servant, staring with wide-open eyes at the scarlet letter. "But he is talking to a minister and to other gentlemen. You cannot see him now."

"I will enter anyway," answered Hester.

The mother and little Pearl were admitted into the entrance hall. The governor was returning from a walk in his garden with Mr Wilson.

Behind the governor and Mr Wilson came two other guests: the young Reverend Arthur Dimmesdale and old Roger Chillingworth. Chillingworth had settled in the town about three years ago, and worked as a physician. He was a friend of the young minister, whose health had been suffering lately.

As the governor entered the hall, he immediately noticed the little scarlet figure before him. "How did this guest enter my hall?" he asked.

"Indeed," cried Mr Wilson, "who is this little scarlet bird? Who are you and why has your mother dressed you in this strange way?"

1. **crimson** : purple-red color.
2. **unpremeditated offshoot** : unplanned product or branch.
3. **bosom** : the front of a person's chest.

"I am mother's child," answered the scarlet vision, "and my name is Pearl."

Governor Bellingham looked sternly at Hester and said, "Hester Prynne, we have been worried about your child's salvation. Is it right for you, who has fallen into sin, to be responsible for the religious and moral instruction of your child? This child needs to be dressed soberly, [1] disciplined strictly and instructed in the truths of heaven and earth. What can you do for her?"

"I can teach my little Pearl what I have learned from this!" answered Hester, laying her finger on the scarlet letter.

"Woman, it is because of this badge [2] of shame that we want to give the child to other hands."

"Nevertheless," said the mother calmly, "this badge has taught me, and is teaching me at this moment, lessons that can make my child wiser and better."

"We will judge carefully," said Governor Bellingham. "Reverend Wilson, examine Pearl and see whether she has had the Christian instruction for a child of her age."

The old minister sat down and tried to draw [3] Pearl near him.

"Pearl," he said solemnly, "can you tell me who made you?" Now Pearl knew very well who made her because Hester had talked to her about the Heavenly Father. For a child of three years old, she knew many things concerning catechism. [4] But she refused to answer Reverend Wilson's question. After putting her finger in her mouth and refusing to speak, she finally said that she had not been made at all — she had been picked off a bush of wild roses by her mother!

Old Roger Chillingworth smiled and whispered something in

1. **soberly** : reasonably and seriously.
2. **badge** : sign.
3. **draw** : move, pull.
4. **catechism** : summary of the principles of a religion in the form of questions and answers.

the young minister's ear. Hester looked at Chillingworth and saw how much uglier he had become.

"This is awful!" cried the governor. "Here is a child of three years old who does not know who made her! We do not need to discuss the matter any further."

Hester picked up Pearl and held the child tightly in her arms. "God gave me this child! She is my only happiness. She keeps me alive! You will not take her! I will die first!"

"My poor woman, the child will be well cared for!"

"God gave her to me," repeated Hester raising her voice. "I will not give her up." She suddenly turned to Mr Dimmesdale and said, "Speak for me! You are my pastor [1] and are responsible for my soul! You know me better than these men. You know what is in my heart. Speak for me!"

Reverend Dimmesdale looked thinner and more troubled than when he had questioned Hester three years earlier.

"There is truth in what she says," began the minister with a sweet, tremulous, [2] but powerful voice. "God gave her the child and the instinctive knowledge of its nature and needs, which no other mortal can possess. Moreover, there is a quality of sacredness [3] in the relation between this mother and child."

"How is that, Master Dimmesdale?" interrupted the governor.

"This child has come from the hand of God to work in many ways upon the mother's heart. It was meant to be a blessing; the one blessing in her life! This child was meant to keep her mother's soul alive, and to preserve her from blacker depths of sin. Therefore, it is good for this poor, sinful woman to care for the child. The child will

1. **pastor** : leader of a Christian group.
2. **tremulous** : shaking slightly.
3. **sacredness** : religious or holy quality.

remind her of her fall. Let us follow God's wish."

"You speak with a strange earnestness," [1] said old Roger Chillingworth, smiling at him.

"My young brother has spoken well," said Reverend Wilson.

"Indeed, he has," answered the governor. "We will leave the matter as it now stands. The child, however, must be examined in catechism, either by Reverend Wilson or Master Dimmesdale. And at the right time, she must go to school and to meeting." [2]

After having spoken, the young minister stood by the window and looked out. Pearl, that wild little elf, [3] went to him, took his hand in both of hers and put it against her cheek. The minister looked down, laid his hand on the child's head and then kissed her forehead.

"A strange child!" said old Roger Chillingworth. "It's easy to see the mother's part in her. Would it be so difficult to analyze the child's nature and then try to guess who the father is?"

"No, it would be sinful," said Reverend Wilson. "It is better to leave the mystery as we find it, unless Providence reveals it to us."

Everything was satisfactorily concluded, and Hester and Pearl left the governor's mansion. As they went down the steps, they met Mistress Hibbins, the governor's bad-tempered sister, who was later executed [4] as a witch.

She looked at Hester and asked, "Will you go to the forest with us tonight? I promised the Black Man [5] that you would come."

"I must stay at home to look after Pearl. If they had taken her away from me, I would have gone with you willingly, and I would have signed my name in the Black Man's book with my own blood."

1. **earnestness** : seriousness, sincerity.
2. **meeting** : (here) religious service or religious meeting.
3. **elf** : small creature with magical powers.
4. **executed** : killed as lawful punishment.
5. **Black Man** : Satan, devil.

Comprehension

FCE ❶ **Choose the answer, A, B, C or D, which you think fits best according to the text.**

1. The governor and other leading citizens wanted to
   A ☐   send Hester away from Boston.
   B ☐   send Pearl to catechism class.
   C ☐   save Hester's soul.
   D ☐   take Pearl away from Hester.

2. They felt that Hester
   A ☐   was not capable of raising her child in a Christian way.
   B ☐   did not possess the elements of salvation.
   C ☐   was not a good church member.
   D ☐   was the wife of the devil.

3. Hester said that she could teach Pearl
   A ☐   a foreign language.
   B ☐   what she had learned from the scarlet letter.
   C ☐   the truth about heaven and earth.
   D ☐   catechism.

4. When Governor Bellingham decided to take Pearl away from her mother, Hester
   A ☐   accepted his decision.
   B ☐   grabbed Pearl and ran out of the mansion.
   C ☐   asked Reverend Dimmesdale to intervene.
   D ☐   began crying desperately.

5. After Reverend Dimmesdale had convinced the governor to let Hester keep the child,
   A ☐   Hester went to thank the minister.
   B ☐   Pearl took his hand in both of hers.
   C ☐   Pearl kissed his hand.
   D ☐   Roger Chillingworth disagreed with him.

6. The Black Man was believed to be
   A ☐   Hester's lover.
   B ☐   a mysterious minister.
   C ☐   an Indian.
   D ☐   the devil.

Grammar

The third conditional

Look at this sentence from Chapter 6:

*If they **had taken** her away from me, I **would have gone** with you willingly, and I **would have signed** my name in the Black Man's book with my own blood.*

We use the third conditional to talk about something that *didn't happen* or a situation that *didn't exist* in the past.

We use the Past Perfect in the "if" clause and the Past Conditional in the main clause. Look at these examples:

*If Hester **had not sinned**, she **wouldn't have worn** the scarlet letter.*

*The governor **would have taken** Pearl away from her mother if Reverend Dimmesdale **had not intervened.***

2 **Look at this dialogue between Roger Chillingworth and Hester. Complete it using the Past Perfect and *would have*.**

Hester: If I (*not be*) 1 .... so poor, I (*not marry*)
2 .... you, Roger.

Roger: If I (*listen*) 3 .... to my old mother, I (*remain*)
4 .... alone. She was very wise, and she knew
you could not be trusted.

Hester: Your mother (*trust*) 5 .... me if she (*know*)
6 .... me better. I am not a faithless person. If
you (*not send*) 7 .... me to Boston alone, this
(*not happen*) 8 ....

Roger: If you (*avoid*) 9 .... temptation, we (*be*)
10 .... a respectable family. But we are not!
We are a disgrace!

Hester: If the judges (*decide*) 11 .... on the death
penalty, I (*not disgrace*) 12 .... our family.

FCE 3 **Read the text below and look carefully at each line. Some of the lines are correct, and some have a word which should not be there. If a line is correct, put a tick (✓) by the number. If a line has a word which should not be there, write the word. There are two examples at the beginning (0) and (00).**

0   Hester went to Governor Bellingham's mansion accompanied by

00 with Pearl, who was wearing an embroidered crimson dress.

1   When they arrived at the mansion the governor had the guests.

2   There were Reverend Wilson, Reverend Dimmesdale and old

3   Roger Chillingworth. Chillingworth worked as a physician in the

4   town where he had been settled three years earlier. He had

5   become a friend of Reverend Dimmesdale he who had not been

6   feeling well lately. The Governor and Reverend Wilson were

7   surprised to see little Pearl before of them. Governor Bellingham

8   asked Reverend Wilson to examine Pearl. When Pearl did not to

9   answer his question correctly, the Governor decided to take Pearl

10 away from Hester. However, Hester asked to Reverend

11 Dimmesdale to speak for her. He spoke at with great sincerity and

12 convinced the governor and Reverend Wilson to permit to Hester

13 to keep Pearl. After this, Pearl took the minister's hand and put it

14 against with her cheek. He put his hand on her head and kissed

15 on her forehead.

0 ...✓..... 00 ..with.. 1 .... 2 .... 3 .... 4 ....

5 .... 6 .... 7 .... 8 .... 9 .... 10 ....

11 .... 12 .... 13 .... 14 .... 15 ....

Salem and Witchcraft

Belief in witches and witchcraft was common in Europe and New England during the 17th century. Before the dramatic Salem witchcraft trials, almost 300 New Englanders (mostly lower-class, middle-aged women, spinsters [1] or widows) had been accused of witchcraft, and more than 30 had been hanged. However, the Salem trials exceeded all precedents [2] in their intensity.

In 1692, a few adolescent girls became entranced listeners of voodoo [3] stories told by Tituba, a slave from the West Indies.

Examination of a witch (1855) by Thomas H. Matteson.

1. **spinsters** : older women who aren't married.
2. **precedents** : earlier cases that are regarded as examples.
3. **voodoo** : magical.

Suddenly, these girls began acting strangely — they shouted, barked, groveled, [1] twitched [2] — without any apparent reason. The town doctor concluded that they had been bewitched. [3] The girls pointed to Tituba and two white women as the culprits. [4]

The townspeople were seized by panic as the word spread that the devil was among them. At a hearing before the magistrates, the "bewitched" girls shrieked and rolled on the floor in convulsive fits as they were questioned by the magistrates. In the midst of this hysteria, [5] Tituba shocked her listeners by confessing to the charge and accusing many others in the community of performing the devil's work.

At this point, the crazed girls began accusing dozens of townspeople, including several of the most respected members of the Puritan community.

After a few months, the Salem prison was filled with townspeople — men, women and children — all accused of practicing witchcraft. There was general hysteria everywhere in the area.

Within ten months, 19 people had been hanged and more than 100 had been put in prison. One man, Giles Corey, was pressed to death with heavy stones. Sarah Good, who was hanged on July 19, 1692, put a curse on Reverend Noyes. She told him that if she was hanged, he would have blood to drink. Tradition says that twenty-five years later, Reverend Noyes died of a throat hemorrhage. [6]

As the accusations spread beyond Salem, colonial leaders began to worry that the witch-hunts were out of control. When the bewitched

---

1. **groveled** : lay or moved face downwards in sign of abject humility or fear.
2. **twitched** : moved uncontrollably.
3. **bewitched** : possessed by an evil spirit.
4. **culprits** : the people responsible, usually for a crime.
5. **hysteria** : extreme fear that cannot be controlled.
6. **hemorrhage** : a large flow of blood from a damaged blood vessel.

girls accused Samuel Willard, the devoted pastor of Boston's First Church and president of Harvard College, the magistrates decided that something was wrong.

Witch Hill (The Salem Martyr [1]) 1869
by Thomas Satterwhite Noble (1835-1907).

1. **martyr** : person who is killed because of his or her (religious) beliefs.

The governor himself intervened [1] when his own wife was accused of worshipping the devil. He disbanded [2] the special court that was responsible for the witch-hunt and released the remaining suspects. A year after it had started, the terrible witch-hunt was finally over. There was never another witch-hunt like it in the New England colonies. In Europe, however, witches were still being executed in the 18th century.

Arthur Miller, the famous American playwright, [3] wrote a play about the Salem witch trials, called *The Crucible*. A film, based on the play, was produced in 1996.

1. **intervened** : interfered so as to change the result.
2. **disbanded** : broke up an organization.
3. **playwright** : a person who writes plays.

FCE 1 **Read the text below and think of the word which best fits each space. Use only one word for each space.**

Belief in witches and (**1**) .... was common in Europe and New England during the (**2**) .... century. In 1692 a few (**3**) .... girls listened to the (**4**) .... stories told by Tituba, a slave (**5**) .... the West Indies. Suddenly these girls began acting (**6**) .... The town (**7**) .... said that they had been (**8**) .... The girls (**9**).................. Tituba and two white women. There was (**10**) .... in the town and the people thought that the (**11**) .... was among them.

When the girls were before the magistrates they rolled on the (**12**) .... in convulsive fits. Tituba confessed and accused other (**13**) .... in the community of doing the devil's work. Soon the Salem (**14**) .... was filled with townspeople who were accused of (**15**) .... witchcraft. (**16**) .... people were hanged. When the governor's (**17**) .... was accused of witchcraft, the governor disbanded the special (**18**) .... and the witch-hunt was finally (**19**) ....

Before reading

FCE 1 Listen to the first part of Chapter Seven and choose the best answer, A, B or C.

1. Who possessed the lock and key to Hester's silence?

   A ☐ Reverend Dimmesdale

   B ☐ Reverend Wilson

   C ☐ Roger Chillingworth

2. Why were the townspeople worried?

   A ☐ Because Reverend Dimmesdale's health was failing.

   B ☐ Because Roger Chillingworth wanted to leave Boston.

   C ☐ Because Reverend Dimmesdale wanted to leave Boston.

3. Reverend Dimmesdale and his physician

   A ☐ often went to Salem together.

   B ☐ took long walks together.

   C ☐ always read the Bible together.

4. According to Chillingworth, the illnesses of the body

   A ☐ can be cured with Indian medicines.

   B ☐ can rarely be cured.

   C ☐ are connected with the problems of the heart and mind.

5. What did Reverend Dimmesdale's friends arrange?

   A ☐ for him to share the same house as Chillingworth

   B ☐ for him to take a trip with Chillingworth

   C ☐ for him to have dinner together with Chillingworth

CHAPTER **SEVEN**

The Leech [1] and his Patient

Under the name of Roger Chillingworth was hidden another name, which Chillingworth had decided never to use. He was unknown to all, except to Hester, and he possessed the lock and key of her silence.

Roger Chillingworth set up his residence in the town of Boston, and he became the physician of the settlement. The townspeople considered themselves fortunate to have such a learned physician in their town. During the period of Indian

---

1. **leech** : (arch.) doctor, but also a person who holds on to another.

captivity [1] he had gained considerable knowledge of the medicinal properties of native herbs and roots.

Chillingworth had chosen Reverend Dimmesdale, who was greatly admired, as his spiritual guide. At about this time, Reverend Dimmesdale's health began to fail. The townspeople were very worried about this. He had become very thin and his cheeks were terribly pale. He often put his hand over his heart in sign of pain.

Therefore, the townspeople thought it was an absolute miracle that Dr. Chillingworth had come to cure their reverend. He became the reverend's medical adviser. Together, they took long walks in the forest and along the seashore. Both were learned, intelligent men and they were glad to exchange their ideas on different topics. Intellectually, it was a breath of fresh air for the reverend.

Thus Roger Chillingworth, the kind and friendly physician, got to know his patient very well — too well. Chillingworth believed that the illnesses of the body are usually connected with the problems of the heart and mind.

A man burdened with a secret should avoid the intimate company of his physician because if the physician possesses intuition, [2] sooner or later the secret will transpire. [3] Chillingworth felt that Reverend Dimmesdale possessed a secret that he was carefully guarding.

After some time, upon a hint from Roger Chillingworth, the friends of Reverend Dimmesdale arranged that the two should share the same house. In this way, every moment of the minister's life would pass under the investigating eye of his anxious

1. **captivity** : when people are kept somewhere and not allowed to leave.
2. **intuition** : an ability to know something immediately.
3. **transpire** : become known.

physician. The townspeople were relieved because they felt that the reverend would finally be in good hands.

END

This new home was with a pious [1] widow of good social rank. The kind widow gave the sickly [2] reverend a front apartment with a sunny exposure. On the other side of the house, old Chillingworth arranged his study and laboratory.

As time went on, a part of the community began to see the old physician as a mysterious figure. There was an aged craftsman who said he had seen the same physician in London about thirty years earlier.

Others said that Roger Chillingworth's aspect had undergone a remarkable change since he began living with Reverend Dimmesdale. At first, his expression had been calm, meditative and scholarly. Now there was something ugly and evil in his face that became more evident as the days passed. According to these people, the fire in his laboratory was fed with infernal fuel. Sometimes a blue, ghastly [3] light burned in his eyes.

To sum up the matter, a good majority of the townspeople believed that Reverend Dimmesdale, like many other holy people, was haunted either by Satan himself or by Satan's messenger, disguised as old Roger Chillingworth.

Throughout his life, old Chillingworth had been a calm, kindly individual. He had never been a warm person, but he was an upright [4] man. He had begun his investigation with the impartial [5] integrity of a judge, but as time went on, he became emotionally involved. He was seized by a terrible fascination that never again set him free. He became obsessed.

---

1. **pious** : religious.
2. **sickly** : not healthy, weak.
3. **ghastly** : causing great fear.
4. **upright** : honest, responsible.
5. **impartial** : fair.

The Scarlet Letter

He dug incessantly [1] into the poor clergyman's heart, like a miner searching for gold. He groped [2] along as stealthily [3] as a thief. Reverend Dimmesdale, who was extremely sensitive, became aware that something inimical [4] had entered his life. He was suspicious of all mankind. He trusted no man as his friend, but he was not able to recognize his enemy when he actually appeared. Therefore, he continued being Chillingworth's close friend. Dimmesdale often visited the physician's laboratory and watched the processes by which weeds and roots were converted into potent medicines.

One day, while he was in the physician's laboratory, he asked, "Where did you find those weeds with such a dark leaf?"

"I found them growing on a grave that had no tombstone. These ugly weeds probably grew out of a dead man's heart — a heart that hid some hideous [5] secret that was buried with him; a secret that he should have confessed during his lifetime."

"Perhaps," said the reverend, "he earnestly wanted to but he could not."

"Why not?" asked Chillingworth, observing the reverend closely.

"The human heart hides our most hideous secrets, and it must do so until that Last Day. [6] Then, with immeasurable joy, all men will reveal their sins before the Heavenly Father. Only the Divine power can peer [7] into the heart to discover its secrets."

---

1. **incessantly** : continually.
2. **groped** : felt or searched about for something.
3. **stealthily** : secretly, quietly, cat-like.
4. **inimical** : hostile.
5. **hideous** : dreadful, strange, unpleasant.
6. **Last Day** : Judgment Day, in religion, the day when God will judge all men.
7. **peer** : look very carefully.

The Leech and his Patient

"But why not reveal them here? Why shouldn't the guilty ones get rid of [1] their burden and receive this immeasurable joy here on earth?"

"Most sinners do," said the reverend, gripping his breast. "Many, many a poor soul has confided in me, not only on the death-bed. And after such an outpouring, the sinner experienced immense [2] relief."

"Yet some men bury their secrets," observed the calm physician.

"True, there are such men," answered the reverend.

"These men are afraid to take up the shame that belongs to them," said Chillingworth. "Such men deceive themselves!"

The physician continued examining the plants that he had gathered. Reverend Dimmesdale watched him and then said, "Do you think my health is improving with your remedies? Please speak frankly."

The physician was still busy with the plants, but kept a wary [3] eye on the reverend. "Your disorder is a strange one. Have you told me everything I need to know in order to cure you? Are you hiding anything from me?"

"How can you ask me this?" said the minister.

"To speak very plainly, I think your bodily disease is only a symptom [4] of a spiritual ailment. [5] Please pardon me, sir, if my speech offends you."

"I presume you do not deal in medicine for the soul!" said the reverend, hastily rising from his chair.

---

1. **get rid of** : free oneself of something unpleasant.
2. **immense** : extremely large in degree.
3. **wary** : attentive, suspicious, cautious.
4. **symptom** : feeling of illness or physical or mental change.
5. **ailment** : illness.

The Scarlet Letter

Chillingworth went on in an unaltered [1] tone, "If you want your physician to heal the evil of your body, you must first reveal to him the trouble in your soul."

"No! Not to you! Not to an earthly physician!" cried Reverend Dimmesdale passionately, with a kind of fierceness. "Not to you! If my soul is troubled, I will open myself to the Physician of the soul! Who are you to meddle [2] in this matter—to put yourself between the sufferer and his God?"

With a frantic gesture, he rushed out of the room.

"It is good that this has happened," said Chillingworth to himself. "Nothing is lost. We'll be friends again. But I have seen how passion takes hold of this man. As with one passion, so with another!"

After a few hours, the reverend apologized to his physician for his outburst. [3] He asked Chillingworth to continue curing his health. Chillingworth agreed and continued his medical supervision.

One day at noon, Reverend Dimmesdale fell asleep in his chair while reading a book. Old Chillingworth came into his room, but did not awaken the reverend. He laid his hand on the reverend's chest and thrust [4] aside the vestment that had always covered it. Dimmesdale continued sleeping.

After a moment, the physician turned away with a wild look of wonder, joy and horror! He threw up his arms and stamped his foot on the floor! He behaved like Satan himself when a soul is lost to heaven and won into his kingdom.

1. **unaltered** : staying the same.
2. **meddle** : interfere.
3. **outburst** : sudden explosion of feeling.
4. **thrust** : pushed.

Comprehension

1 **Answer the following questions.**

  a. How did Roger Chillingworth enter into Reverend Dimmesdale's life?

  b. Why was Roger Chillingworth so deeply interested in the clergyman's life and secrets?

  c. How did Chillingworth's aspect change after he began living with the reverend?

  d. Was Reverend Dimmesdale aware of an evil presence in his life?

  e. What made the reverend explode in anger? How did Chillingworth react?

  f. What made the physician throw up his arms and stamp his foot on the floor?

Grammar

The passive

Look at these examples from Chapter 7:

*The fire in his laboratory **was fed** with infernal fuel.*

*Reverend Dimmesdale ... **was haunted** either **by** Satan himself, or **by** Satan's messenger.*

Both of these sentences are in the passive.
- **We use the passive when the person or thing doing the action isn't important, isn't known, or is understood.**
- **We form the passive by using a form of *be* and a past participle.**
- **Only verbs that have an object can have a passive form.**
- **If we are using the passive and we want to mention the person or thing that performs the action, we use *by*.**

2 It's 1853 and you are a young journalist who works for the *Boston Times*. You are interviewing Nathaniel Hawthorne, who is now a very famous writer. You want Hawthorne to tell you about the changes Boston has undergone in the past 30 years. Rewrite his description using a passive construction.

Interviewer : How has Boston changed in the past 30 years, Mr Hawthorne?

a. Well, they have built an addition to the old port recently.

....

b. The port workers unload the ships with new machinery, and not by hand.

....

c. They have expanded the downtown area greatly.

....

d. They're building a new town hall near the river.

....

e. They'll probably finish it in the spring.

....

f. Dr John Peabody, the surgeon, opened a new hospital at the east end of town.

....

g. His brother, William, directs it.

....

Writing

3 Choose the words from the box that best describe Roger Chillingworth before and after he was seized by his terrible suspicions. Then choose the words that best describe Reverend Dimmesdale all through the story. Some words can be used more than once. Write 3 short paragraphs describing these characters.

> learned   ugly   suspicious   intelligent   scholarly
> eloquent speaker   passionate   wary   enemy in disguise
> kindly   upright   evil   sickly   admired   sensitive
> trusted no one   meditative   thin   troubled   pale
> calm   religious   deceiver

Both men were .... and ....

Before his terrible suspicions, Roger Chillingworth was:

....

....

....

....

After his terrible suspicions, he became:

....

....

....

....

Throughout the story, Reverend Dimmesdale is:

....

....

....

....

The Word "Witch"

To understand the Salem witch trials, it is necessary to know the 17th-century definition of the word "witch". In England and New England, it was believed that a witch was a person who had made a pact [1] with Satan. The pact involved an exchange of a soul for special evil powers, with which other mortals could be tormented.

Victims of witchcraft claimed to see horrible visions, exhibit strange

Passe (Martin)

behavior and experience physical pain. These victims were said to be bewitched. The person who was accused of causing this was arrested and tried in a court of law. Under the English legal system of the 17th century, the person who was found guilty of practicing witchcraft was hanged.

The word "witch" has another important definition. People who practice the pagan religion of Wicca (similar to the word "witch"), trace their beliefs to Pre-Christian times.

Wicca is a religion based on Nature, and it worships a Father God and Mother Goddess. Wicca followers are not involved in any type of evil or witchcraft.

Finally, the word "witch" creates another image in our minds: the stereotype [2] of an old, ugly lady, dressed in black, who wears a pointed hat and flies through the night sky on her broom. She is usually accompanied by a black cat. This is the cartoon interpretation of the "witch" that we see at Halloween because Halloween originated as a Celtic festivity. Witches were a part of Celtic culture.

1. **pact** : agreement.   2. **stereotype** : fixed idea.

FCE ❶ Choose the answer, A, B, C or D, which you think fits best according to the text.

1. In the 17th century it was believed that a witch
   A ☐ was a prophet.
   B ☐ had magic powers.
   C ☐ had made a pact with Satan.
   D ☐ could predict the future.

2. Making a pact with the devil involved
   A ☐ an exchange of a soul for special evil powers.
   B ☐ worshipping Satan.
   C ☐ offering a human sacrifice.
   D ☐ signing a special document.

3. Being bewitched meant
   A ☐ having drunk a special drink.
   B ☐ practicing witchcraft with other witches.
   C ☐ making a pact with the devil.
   D ☐ exhibiting strange behavior, experiencing pain.

4. Under the English legal system of the 17th century, the punishment for witchcraft was
   A ☐ ten years in prison.
   B ☐ burning at the stake.
   C ☐ hanging.
   D ☐ life imprisonment.

5. Wicca is a pagan religion based on
   A ☐ Nature.
   B ☐ witchcraft.
   C ☐ human and animal sacrifice.
   D ☐ astrology.

6. Witches are symbolic of Halloween because
   A ☐ Wicca is the ancient name for Halloween.
   B ☐ Halloween originated as a Celtic festivity and witches were a part of the Celtic culture.
   C ☐ most witchcraft is practiced on Halloween.
   D ☐ they invented Halloween.

CHAPTER **EIGHT**

The Interior of a Heart

 After the incident last described, the relationship between the clergyman and the physician changed profoundly, although externally it seemed the same. Roger Chillingworth appeared calm, gentle and passionless, as always. But there was now a certain malice in this old man that led him to imagine a more intimate revenge than any mortal had ever inflicted on an enemy. Chillingworth saw and understood every movement of Dimmesdale's soul. He became the chief actor in the poor minister's interior world. He could manipulate [1] the reverend as he chose because he knew the spring that controlled the engine.

1. **manipulate** : control.

The Scarlet Letter

All this was accomplished with perfect subtlety. Although the minister felt an evil influence watching over him, he could never suspect its real nature. At times he looked doubtfully, fearfully, and even with horror and hatred at the deformed physician. His entire being was odious [1] to the minister.

Nevertheless as a matter of principle, the reverend continued his habits of social familiarity with the old physician. This gave Chillingworth a constant opportunity to perfect his revenge on his unsuspecting victim.

Reverend Dimmesdale suffered from ill health, was tormented by a troubled soul and was a victim of the machinations [2] of his worst enemy. In spite of all this, he achieved a brilliant popularity as a pastor. His intellectual gifts and his power of communicating emotion were kept alive by the anguish of his daily life.

It was the heavy burden he carried in his heart that enabled him to understand the sinners of his congregation so well. He was considered a miracle of holiness.

This public veneration tortured him! He longed to speak out from his own pulpit and tell the people what he really was: "I, your pastor, whom you venerate and trust, am a profanation [3] and a lie!"

More than once, Reverend Dimmesdale had gone to the pulpit with the purpose of revealing his true self. More than once he had cleared his throat and had actually spoken! Spoken! But how?

He told his congregation that he was completely vile and disgusting, the worst of sinners and unworthy [4] in every way. Wouldn't the people take him out of the pulpit? Not so! They appreciated him even more! "He is a saint on earth! If he sees sins

1. **odious** : extremely unpleasant.
2. **machinations** : plans for doing harm.
3. **profanation** : a lack of respect.
4. **unworthy** : contemptible, inferior.

in his own white soul, what a horrid spectacle if he ever saw mine!" they said among themselves.

The minister knew — subtle, but remorseful hypocrite that he was — how his vague confession would be viewed. He spoke the truth and transformed it into a falsehood. And yet he loved the truth and hated lies. Therefore, above all things, he hated his miserable self!

In the reverend's secret closet, under lock and key, there was a whip. His inner troubles led him to whip his own shoulders, while he laughed bitterly.

It was also his custom to fast. [1] He fasted as an act of penance, [2] until his knees trembled. At night, instead of sleeping, he kept vigils. [3] During these long vigils, he studied himself in the mirror. He had visions of angels, of demons, of dead friends of his youth, of his parents. He also had visions of Hester with little Pearl in her scarlet dress, pointing to her mother's scarlet letter and then to the minister's own breast.

Reverend Dimmesdale lived a life of misery, a life of falsehood. The only truth that continued to give him a real existence on earth was the anguish [4] of his soul.

On one of those ugly nights, a new thought came to his mind. He dressed with care, went down the staircase quietly, opened the door and went out.

Walking in the shadow of a dream, Reverend Dimmesdale reached the platform where seven years before Hester Prynne had lived through her first hour of public ignominy.

It was a cloudy night in early May. The town was asleep. Why

1. **fast** : eat no food for a certain period of time.
2. **penance** : an act showing that one regrets something that one has done.
3. **vigils** : staying awake during the night.
4. **anguish** : agony, anxiety, torment.

had the minister come here? He had been driven by the impulses of Remorse and Cowardice: [1] Remorse pushed him to confession, while Cowardice pulled him back with her tremulous grip.

While standing on the scaffold in this vain show of expiation, [2] the reverend was overcome by a horrible feeling — it was as if the universe was gazing at a scarlet token on his naked breast, right over his heart.

Without realizing it, he shrieked [3] aloud! It was a cry that went ringing through the night.

"It is done," he muttered, covering his face with his hands. "The whole town will awaken and find me here!" But the town did not awaken.

Suddenly, in the dark of the night, he heard a light, childish laugh — he recognized little Pearl's voice.

"Pearl! Little Pearl!" he cried. Then, with a softer voice, he said, "Hester! Hester Prynne! Are you there?"

"Yes, it is Hester Prynne," she replied, approaching the platform.

"Where are you coming from?" asked the minister.

"I have been at Governor Winthrop's [4] deathbed to take the measurements for his deathrobe."

"Come up here, Hester, you and little Pearl," said the minister. "You both have been here before, but I was not with you. Let us stand all three together."

She ascended the steps hesitantly, and stood on the platform, holding Pearl by the hand. The minister took the child's other hand. The moment that he did so, a rush of new life poured into his heart and rushed through his veins. It was as if the mother

---

1. **Cowardice** : lack of courage.
2. **expiation** : an act of showing regret for bad behaviour.
3. **shrieked** : gave a wild, painful cry.
4. **Governor Winthrop** : the founder of the Puritan town of Boston.

and child were communicating their vital warmth to his half-torpid [1] system. The three formed an electric chain.

Suddenly, a bright light lit up the cloudy sky. It was undoubtedly a meteor flying through the sky.

In those days it was common to interpret the appearance of meteors as revelations from a supernatural source. As Reverend Dimmesdale looked up at the sky that had been lit by the meteor, he saw an immense letter A — marked with lines of dull red light.

While the reverend was gazing up at the sky, he was perfectly aware that little Pearl was pointing her finger at old Roger Chillingworth, who stood not far from the scaffold.

"Who is that man, Hester?" gasped [2] the reverend, filled with terror. "Do you know this man? I hate him, Hester!"

She remembered her oath [3] and was silent.

"My soul shivers at the sight of that man. He fills me with horror. Who is he?" muttered the reverend again.

Approaching the platform with a malevolent [4] expression, Chillingworth said, "Pious Master Dimmesdale, can this be you? We men of study dream in our working moments, and walk in our sleep. Come, my dear friend, let me lead you home."

"How did you know I was here?" asked the reverend.

"I have spent most of the night at the deathbed of Governor Winthrop, trying to ease his suffering. Come with me, Reverend, we must go home now," said Chillingworth. "Tomorrow is the Sabbath!"

The next day was the Sabbath and Reverend Dimmesdale preached his most powerful sermon. [5] It was the richest and most complete that he had ever addressed to his devoted congregation. [6]

1. **torpid** : dull and slow.
2. **gasped** : took a short quick breath because he was shocked.
3. **oath** : solemn promise.
4. **malevolent** : intending to cause harm.
5. **sermon** : a talk on a religious or moral subject given by a priest.
6. **congregation** : a group of people who attend religious gathering.

Comprehension

1 **Answer the following questions.**

a. How did the relationship between the clergyman and the physician change?

b. Why was Reverend Dimmesdale so successful as a pastor?

c. How did Reverend Dimmesdale "reveal" his true self to his congregation?

d. Why did the minister go to the platform one night?

e. Describe his meeting with Hester and Pearl.

f. What did the reverend say to Hester about Chillingworth?

FCE 2 **Who did what?**

Look back at Chapter Eight and for questions 1-9 choose from the people (A-F).

A = Hester   B = Pearl   C = Dimmesdale

D = Chillingworth   E = meteor   F = congregation

He appeared passionless and calm.	**1.** ....
She pointed her finger at old Chillingworth.	**2.** ....
He felt an evil influence watching over him.	**3.** ....
She was coming from Governor Winthrop's deathbed.	**4.** ....
They venerated their reverend.	**5.** ....
He knew he was a hypocrite.	**6.** ....
He spent most of the night at the deathbed of the governor.	**7.** ....
He hated Chillingworth intensely.	**8.** ....
It lit up the cloudy sky.	**9.** ....

FCE 3 **Read the summary of Chapters Five to Eight and think of the word which best fits each space. Use only one word for each space.**

When Hester Prynne's prison term was finally over she **(1)** .... that she would be **(2)** .... in the world with her child. She was **(3)** .... to leave Boston, but she decided to stay. The Puritan community **(4)** .... her and Pearl. Her only

(**5**) .... with society was through her work; she was considered a (**6**) .... by the townspeople.

Governor Bellingham seriously thought about (**7**) .... Pearl (**8**) .... from Hester. At a (**9**) .... with the governor, Reverend Dimmesdale was able to (**10**) .... him to let Hester keep Pearl since this was (**11**) .... wish.

Roger Chillingworth became Reverend Dimmesdale's medical (**12**) .... and never left him (**13**) .... The minister and the physician even (**14**) .... in the same house. As time went on Chillingworth underwent a hideous (**15**) .... He was convinced that the reverend was (**16**) .... a terrible secret. The reverend had a troubled (**17**) .... but he never revealed his shame to anyone. He told his (**18**) .... that he was a vile sinner, and everyone appreciated him even more. He (**19**) .... his shoulders and fasted as an act of (**20**) ....

One (**21**) .... he met Hester and Pearl on the scaffold, and Chillingworth (**22**) .... them together.

Writing

4 Imagine you are Reverend Dimmesdale. You keep a secret diary about your tormented life. Use the information in this chapter to record the events and emotions of the past few days, and particularly the night on the scaffold. Use no more than 120-180 words.

Start like this:

May 10. 1649 – My life is becoming more tormented and more difficult. The presence of Roger Chillingworth ....

Grammar

5 **Choose the correct word and fill in the blanks.**

| without | when | while | whom | why | who | where |

a. .... are you coming from?

b. .... standing on the scaffold, the reverend was overcome by a horrible feeling.

c. .... had the minister come here?

d. .... is he?

e. .... realizing it, he shrieked aloud!

f. I, your pastor, ... you venerate and trust, am a profanation and a lie!

g. .... did Hester visit Governor Winthrop's deathbed?

Themes for thought, discussion and writing

A character analysis: Roger Chillingworth

At this point in the story, the personalities of the main protagonists are taking shape. We can see that Roger Chillingworth was a calm, kindly, upright man – a scholar, physician and scientist – who became a victim of his own obsession. This obsession, that Hawthorne calls his "terrible fascination", transformed him. He became evil, ugly, satanic in his ways. His "investigation" had become the only purpose of his life.

6 **Which other famous people in history or in literature had a particular obsession?**

7 **Did this obsession transform their personality? Did they become insane?**

Boston, Heart of the American Revolution

The American Revolution, which gave the 13 American colonies their independence, began on April 19, 1775 in Massachusetts and ended in 1781.

Boston played a very important role in the struggle for American independence. The events that happened in Boston led to the American Revolution. Here are the major events:

1. In the 1760s England passed laws that imposed heavy taxes on the colonists [1] and limited their rights. Bostonians strongly objected.

The Declaration of Independence, July 4, 1776 by John Trumbull.

1. **imposed heavy taxes on the colonists** : placed heavy taxes officially on the colonists.

2. In 1768, riots led to the occupation of Boston by British soldiers. The colonists disliked the constant presence of British troops.

   An angry crowd threw snowballs filled with ice and stones at some British soldiers. The soldiers immediately fired into the crowd, killing five men. This became known as the Boston Massacre. [1]

3. The English Tea Act of 1773 caused great disapproval in the colonies. To protest against this new tax, a group of Bostonians disguised themselves as Mohawk Indians, boarded three ships in the harbor and threw 342 crates [2] of tea into the waters of Boston Harbor. A crowd of colonists watched and cheered. This was the famous Boston Tea Party.

   In response to this, Britain closed the port of Boston. This, of course, created severe economic damage since Boston depended on sea trade.

4. Colonists in and around Boston started organizing armies. They wanted to be prepared to fight if necessary.

5. In the nearby town of Lexington, the first shots of the American Revolution were fired in April 1775.

6. American independence was formally declared by Massachusetts on July 4, 1776. At that time, the 13 American colonies were: Massachusetts, New Hampshire, Rhode Island, Connecticut, New York, New Jersey, Pennsylvania, Delaware, Maryland, Virginia, North Carolina, South Carolina, Georgia.

---

1. **massacre** : an act of killing a large number of people.
2. **crates** : big wooden boxes.

The Declaration of Independence was read to the colonists from the balcony of the Old State House in Boston. The Old State House can be visited as part of Boston's Freedom Trail Walk. Along this historic walk, there are seven important historical sites to visit, each connected with the American Revolution.

1 **Decide whether the sentences are true (T) or false (F). Correct the false ones.**

		T	F
a.	The American Revolution began in Massachusetts in 1781.	☐	☐
b.	Bostonians opposed heavy taxation from Britain.	☐	☐
c.	During the Boston Tea Party, many Indians attacked a ship with a cargo of tea.	☐	☐
d.	British soldiers killed five colonists during the Boston Tea Party.	☐	☐
e.	The colonists in Massachusetts had organized armies and were ready to fight if necessary.	☐	☐
f.	The first shots of the American Revolution were fired in Boston, in April 1775.	☐	☐
g.	On July 4, 1776, America declared its independence from Britain.	☐	☐

CHAPTER **NINE**

Hester and the Physician

 After having met Reverend Dimmesdale on the platform, Hester was shocked by his deteriorated physical and mental condition. In seven years he had undergone a frightening change for the worse. A secret enemy was continually at his side, disguised as a friend and helper. She decided that it was her responsibility to help him.

During the past seven years, Hester's position in the community had changed. She silently accepted her isolation and her shame. She was a self-ordained Sister of Mercy! [1] She

---

1. **self-ordained Sister of Mercy** : person who helps the sick and the poor of her own free will.

constantly helped the poor, the sick and the afflicted. [1] Many people refused to interpret the scarlet A with its original meaning. They said it meant Able. It took a longer time for the rulers of the community to acknowledge [2] Hester's good qualities.

The townspeople had forgiven her for her frailty. They had begun to look upon the scarlet letter as a token of her many good deeds.

The symbol had had a powerful and peculiar effect on Hester. Her physical attractiveness had undergone a sad transformation. Her warm and graceful character had become cold and barren.

In her life of solitude and hopelessness, Hester was free to think about her world and to criticize it. Outwardly, she conformed to [3] the rules of her community, but in the privacy of her mind, she disapproved and detested them. She felt that the whole system of society should be torn down and built up again. If her thoughts had been made public, she would have suffered death for attempting to destroy the Puritan institutions.

Hester decided to meet her former husband, Roger Chillingworth, and do what she could to rescue his victim. One afternoon, while walking with Pearl, she saw the old physician who was gathering roots and herbs. Hester asked Pearl to go to the seashore and play with the shells, while she spoke to the physician.

Hester approached him and said, "I need to speak to you." The physician looked at Hester and said, "Mistress Hester has a word for old Roger Chillingworth!"

1. **the afflicted** : the people who suffer.
2. **acknowledge** : recognize and admit.
3. **conformed to** : obeyed.

Hester and the Physician

Hester looked at Chillingworth and was shocked to see how he had changed in the past years. It was not so much that he had grown older, but that he looked so evil and fierce. There was a glare of red light that came out of his eyes, as if the old man's soul was on fire. In a word, he was the striking example of a man who had transformed himself into a devil. He had devoted seven years of his life to the constant analysis of a tortured heart. And he had derived immense enjoyment in adding fuel to those fiery tortures and gloating [1] over them.

"When we last spoke together seven years ago, you made me promise never to reveal your true identity. At that time, I had no choice. Since that day, you have been behind his every footstep, day and night. You search his thoughts. You dig into his heart. You cause him to die daily a living death. And he still doesn't know who you really are!"

"What evil have I done to this man?" asked Chillingworth. "I have cared for his failing health in every possible way. If I had not cared for him, he would have died!"

"It would have been better if he had died at once!" said Hester.

"Yes, you are right!" cried old Chillingworth. "Never has a man suffered as he has suffered — and before my very eyes! He has felt a constant evil influence, like a curse. But he does not know that I am responsible for his misery. I am the evil fiend!" [2]

"Have you not tortured him enough?" asked Hester. "Has he not paid his debt to you?"

---

1. **gloating** : looking at or thinking about something with enjoyment.
2. **fiend** : devil, evil spirit.

"No, no! He has only increased the debt. Do you remember me, Hester, as I was when you first met me? I was peaceful, innocent, kind and just. Was I not all this?"

"All this and more," said Hester.

"And what am I now?" he cried. "I am a fiend! Who made me so?"

"I, myself!" cried Hester, shuddering. [1] "It was I, not less than he. Why have you not avenged yourself on me?"

"I have left you to the scarlet letter," replied Chillingworth.

"It has avenged you," said Hester. "But now, I must reveal the secret. It is a debt I have with him. Forgive him, and leave his punishment to the Almighty Power. You have been deeply wronged, and it is your privilege to forgive. Do you want to reject this priceless privilege?" There was almost a majestic quality in her despair.

"It is not in my power to pardon. You planted the germ of evil, and now let the black flower blossom. It is our fate. Go and do as you want with that man." He waved his hand and continued gathering herbs.

With great anger, Hester watched him walk away. "Be it sin or not," she said bitterly, "I hate the man!" She wondered how she could have married him. When her heart knew no better, he had persuaded her to be happy by his side. "Yes, I hate him! He betrayed me!"

When Chillingworth had gone, she called back her child. Pearl had been playing with seaweed and had made the letter A, which

---

1. **shuddering** : trembling from fear or cold.

she put on her bosom. "I wonder if mother will ask me what it means!" thought Pearl.

"My little Pearl," said Hester, "the green letter on your young bosom has no purpose. Do you know why your mother wears it?"

"I do!" answered Pearl. "It is for the same reason that the minister keeps his hand over his heart."

"And what is that reason?"

"I have told all I know," Pearl said seriously. She took her mother's hand in both her own, and gazed into her eyes with earnestness. [1] Hester thought that perhaps Pearl had reached an age when she could become a friend for her — a friend with whom to share her sorrow.

Pearl continued to ask her mother about the meaning of the scarlet letter. One day Hester said, "Silly Pearl, there are many things in this world that a child must not ask about. Hold your tongue! Otherwise, I will shut you in a dark closet!" [2]

1. **earnestness** : sincerity.
2. **closet** : a cupboard or a small room.

Comprehension

FCE 1 **Choose the answer, A, B, C or D, which you think fits best according to the text.**

1. After having seen Reverend Dimmesdale on the scaffold, Hester
   - A ☐ started crying.
   - B ☐ was very happy.
   - C ☐ decided to confess her lover's name.
   - D ☐ decided it was her responsibility to help him.

2. After doing good deeds for seven years in the Puritan community,
   - A ☐ she could take off the scarlet letter.
   - B ☐ the townspeople acknowledged her good qualities.
   - C ☐ she went to work for the Sisters of Mercy.
   - D ☐ she left Boston with Pearl.

3. Hester detested and disapproved of the Puritan rules
   - A ☐ and she never went to church.
   - B ☐ and she openly disobeyed them.
   - C ☐ so she decided to flee from Boston.
   - D ☐ but she outwardly conformed to them.

4. Hester met Chillingworth to
   - A ☐ tell him that she wanted to flee.
   - B ☐ warn him that he had an enemy.
   - C ☐ tell him that she wanted to reveal his true identity.
   - D ☐ ask him for a special medicine.

5. Old Chillingworth had devoted the past seven years to
   - A ☐ analyzing the reverend's tortured heart.
   - B ☐ creating new medicines with magic powers.
   - C ☐ studying herbs and roots.
   - D ☐ helping the poor people of Boston.

6. He accused Reverend Dimmesdale of
   - A ☐ being a coward.
   - B ☐ transforming him into an evil fiend.
   - C ☐ being a hypocrite.
   - D ☐ being selfish.

Grammar

Adjectives as nouns

When we talk about a group of people in general, we can use *the* + *adjective* as a noun. *The* + *adjective* is followed by a plural verb. Look at this example from Chapter 9:

She constantly helped the poor, the sick and the afflicted.

We use *the* with some nationality adjectives to talk about the people who live in a country.

* the people who live in Italy = **the Italians**

We can also refer to the general or abstract, such as *the supernatural, the unknown, the unexpected.*

2 Fill in the gaps below using *the* with these adjectives.

rich	blind	French	poor
young	supernatural	elderly	

a. The new museum was designed by ....

b. Since Mary couldn't see, she attended a special school for ....

c. The witches were accused of contacting ....

d. Hester Prynne was judged severely by .... of the town.

e. The .... often have difficulty in finding work.

f. It's only fair that .... should pay higher taxes than ....

Writing

3 **Imagine you are Hester. You want to write in your diary about:**

- the changes you have seen in Reverend Dimmesdale
- the changes you have seen in Roger Chillingworth
- the meeting you had with Chillingworth
- what you plan to do

Use between 120-180 words. You can start like this:

May 25. 1649—I was shocked to see the terrible changes in Reverend Dimmesdale. ....

Themes for thought, discussion and writing

In this story the characters undergo deep physical and mental transformations. We have seen how Chillingworth became an obsessed fiend, the malevolent shadow of the minister.

Hester, too, has changed. Her beauty and warmth have left her. Seven years of isolation, scorn and hopelessness have left their mark. But her natural dignity, compassion and courage have remained untouched.

She has become a "free-thinker", a potential social reformer – in other words, a rebel in her society. Her rebellion, however, is never openly manifested. In the 1640s, the punishment for any type of difference of opinion or rebellion in the Puritan community was death.

4 **How would Hester be considered today? Why?**

☐ rebel   ☐ feminist   ☐ single parent
☐ typical American woman   ☐ community volunteer

5 **How would Hester's "sin" be considered today? Why?**

☐ shameful   ☐ rather normal

☐ not fully approved,   ☐ no one's business but
   but accepted by society   her own

Reverend Dimmesdale's transformation is a complex one. Although his success as a preacher is brilliant and the admiration of his congregation is immense, his heart, soul and mind are on the verge of a catastrophe. Anguish is the only reality he knows. He feels an evil presence enveloping his mind and destroying his frail body, but he isn't able to recognize his enemy. His frightened, childlike remarks to Hester on the scaffold show his deteriorated mental state.

6 **Hawthorne wrote that the reverend was "a subtle, but remorseful hypocrite". How did he express his subtle, remorseful hypocrisy in the following situations?**

a. On the platform with Hester and Pearl. (Chap. 8)

....

....

b. During his sermon. (Chap. 8)

....

....

c. At the governor's mansion. (Chap. 6)

....

....

d. Can you think of other situations in which the reverend acted like a "subtle, but remorseful hypocrite"?

....

....

e. Which aspect(s) of the reverend's character is/are destroying him?

☐ piety   ☐ remorse   ☐ ambition

☐ intelligence   ☐ cowardice   ☐ hypocrisy

Salem Today

Salem's Indian name was Naumkeag, "City of Peace", but it has long been known as the "Witch City" because of the witch trials of 1692.

Salem was a major seaport during the 18th and 19th centuries. Today Salem is internationally recognized as an American historic treasure. It is a small, beautiful town on Massachusetts Bay, about thirty kilometers north of Boston. Its population is approximately 38,000.

Nearly one third of the city has been designated [1] as park land, conservation land and open space. It has one of the most extensive park systems in Massachusetts. Its eighteen miles of shoreline provide six public beaches and numerous recreational activities.

Each year, about one million tourists visit Salem's numerous museums, historic sites and attractions, including Nathaniel

A view of Salem.

1. **designated** : officially chosen.

Hawthorne's birthplace and the Salem Customhouse where he worked.

There are seven important "witch museums" with myths and facts about witchcraft and authentic memorabilia [1] of that epoch. [2]

The original 1692 home of witch trial Judge Jonathan Corwin is still standing, and is open to the public. It is located at 310 Essex Street in Salem.

Over three hundred years have passed since the tragic witch trials, and yet Salem still has an intriguing historic atmosphere.

1 Decide whether these sentences are true (T) or false (F). Correct the false ones.

	T	F
a. Salem's Indian name was Naumkeag, which meant "Witch City".	☐	☐
b. Salem is a small town located about thirty kilometers north of Boston.	☐	☐
c. Nearly one half of the city is designated as park land and open space.	☐	☐
d. Nathaniel Hawthorne's birthplace and the Customhouse where he worked are both historic sites in Salem.	☐	☐
e. There are seventy important "witch museums" in Salem.	☐	☐
f. Jonathan Corwin was the governor during the witchcraft trials.	☐	☐

1. **memorabilia** : things that are very interesting in connection with a famous person or event.
2. **epoch** : a long period of time.

Before reading

FCE **1** **Listen to the first part of Chapter Ten and choose the best answer, A, B or C.**

1. Where did the reverend often take walks?

   A ☐ in the forest and along the seashore

   B ☐ near the scaffold

   C ☐ near the prison

2. Where did Hester and Pearl sit?

   A ☐ on the seashore

   B ☐ on the grass

   C ☐ on a heap of moss

3. Whom did Hester meet once in her life?

   A ☐ the Black Woman

   B ☐ the Black Man

   C ☐ the Black Indian

4. Where did Pearl go?

   A ☐ She went home.

   B ☐ She went to the scaffold.

   C ☐ She went to play.

5. What did Hester and Reverend Dimmesdale talk about at first?

   A ☐ the approaching storm

   B ☐ Pearl

   C ☐ Dimmesdale's poor health

CHAPTER **TEN**

The Pastor and his Parishioner [1]

 Hester was determined to reveal to Reverend Dimmesdale the true identity of Roger Chillingworth. She knew that the reverend often took walks in the forest and along the seashore. Therefore, one day Hester took little Pearl for a walk in the forest. Pearl ran about happily trying to catch the sunshine, and then sat down with her mother on a heap [2] of moss. [3]

"Mother, is there a Black Man who lives in the forest, and

1. **parishioner** : inhabitant of an area having its own church and clergyman.
2. **heap** : small pile.
3. **moss** : soft green plant.

carries a big book where people write their names with their own blood? Did you ever meet him? Oh, tell me!"

Hester looked curiously at little Pearl and replied, "Once in my life I met the Black Man. This scarlet letter is his mark!"

After a vivid conversation with Pearl, Hester heard footsteps in the forest. She knew it was the reverend.

"Pearl, go and play near the brook, [1] while I speak to this person who is walking through the woods. Do not go far away! Stay near the brook."

When the child had gone to play, Hester walked towards the minister, who was coming down the path. He looked tired and weak, and his step was listless. [2] He would have been only too happy to lie down in the dark forest and die.

"Arthur Dimmesdale," Hester said softly.

"Who is there?" said the minister. He took another step and discovered the scarlet letter.

"Hester! Hester Prynne!" he said. "Is it you?"

"Yes!" she replied. They were both awestricken. [3] Arthur Dimmesdale touched Hester's cold hand with his own. They sat down on the heap of moss, and when they had found the strength to speak, made remarks about the approaching storm. They had been separated for so long by fate and circumstances that it took some time before they could open their hearts to each other.

After a while, the minister looked at Hester and said, "Hester, have you found peace?"

She smiled sadly, looked at her bosom and asked, "Have you?"

1. **brook** : small stream.
2. **listless** : without energy.
3. **awestricken** : amazed, speechless.

The Scarlet Letter

"None — nothing but despair! Were I an atheist, [1] a man without a conscience, [2] I might have found peace long ago. But I am a minister! I am so miserable."

"The people revere you and you have certainly worked well among them," said Hester.

"More misery, Hester! I have laughed bitterly at the contrast between what I seem and what I am! And Satan laughs at it! Happy are you, Hester! You wear the scarlet letter openly on your bosom. Mine burns in secret! If only I had a friend, or an enemy, to whom I could tell the truth!"

"You have a friend in me," Hester said. Then, trying desperately to conquer her fears, she said, "You *have* such an enemy, and he lives with you under the same roof!"

The minister jumped to his feet, gasping for breath and clutching [3] at his heart. "What are you saying? An enemy! Under my own roof? What do you mean?"

With her silence of seven years, she had ruined the man she still so passionately loved! Now, she would gladly have died at Arthur Dimmesdale's feet.

"Oh, Arthur," she cried, "forgive me! I have always been truthful, but in this circumstance I had no choice. The old physician — Roger Chillingworth — he was my husband!"

The minister looked at her with unimaginable violence of passion. He had never had a blacker or fiercer frown. [4] He sank down on the ground and buried his face in his hands.

---

1. **atheist** : person who doesn't believe in God.
2. **conscience** : person's awareness of right and wrong with regard to his own thoughts and actions.
3. **clutching** : holding tightly.
4. **frown** : facial expression showing anger.

The Scarlet Letter

"I might have known it! I *did* know it! My heart knew the secret all along. Why didn't I understand? What horror! Woman, you are responsible for this! I cannot forgive you!"

"You will forgive me!" cried Hester, throwing herself beside him. "Let God punish! You will forgive!"

With desperate tenderness, she threw her arms around him and pressed his head against her bosom. His cheek rested on the scarlet letter.

"Will you forgive me?" she repeated over and over again.

After a long silence, he replied, "I forgive you, Hester. I forgive you! May God forgive us both! We are not the worst sinners in the world. That old man's revenge has been blacker than our sin. He has violated the sanctity of the human heart. [1] We never did. But now that Chillingworth knows that you have revealed his secret, will he continue to keep *our* secret?"

"There is a strange secrecy in his nature. I do not think he will reveal our secret," answered Hester.

"And I! How can I live any longer, under the same roof with this deadly enemy?" exclaimed the reverend. "Think for me, Hester! You are strong. Resolve this for me!"

"You must no longer live with this man," said Hester firmly.

"But how can I avoid it? Tell me what I must do. You are strong, Hester," said the reverend.

"Is the world so narrow?" exclaimed Hester, fixing her eyes on the minister's, and exercising a magnetic power over his shattered [2] spirit. "Where does this forest path lead? It goes

---

1. **the sanctity of the human heart** : when something deserves respect.
2. **shattered** : broken, destroyed.

deeper and deeper into the wilderness, where no white man has been. There you are free!

"Then, there is the broad path of the sea! It brought you here, and it can take you back again. You would be out of his power and completely free, if you returned to our native land or to Germany, France or Italy."

"It cannot be! I cannot leave my post. I have no strength or courage to begin a new life," answered the reverend.

"You are crushed under the weight of seven years of misery," replied Hester. "But you will leave it all behind you! Begin everything anew! The future is still full of trial [1] and success. There is happiness to be enjoyed. Exchange this false life of yours for a new one. Preach! [2] Write! Act! Do anything, but do not lie down and die."

"Oh, Hester," cried Dimmesdale, "I must die here! I have no strength or courage left in me to venture [3] into the wide, difficult world *alone*."

He repeated the last word. "*Alone,* Hester."

"You will not go *alone*," she answered, whispering.

Then, all was spoken!

---

1. **trial** : difficult experiences, tests.
2. **preach** : give a religious speech.
3. **venture** : go somewhere that could be dangerous.

Comprehension

1 **Answer the following questions.**

   a. Why did Hester take Pearl for a walk in the forest?

   b. What did Hester tell Pearl about the Black Man who lives in the forest?

   c. Why did it take Hester and the reverend some time before they could open their hearts to each other?

   d. How did Reverend Dimmesdale react to Hester's revelation?

   e. What did Hester advise the reverend to do with his future?

   f. In your opinion, will the reverend begin a new life?

Grammar

2 **Change the following sentences into reported speech, making the necessary changes to the verbs.**

   a. "Hester, have you found peace?" asked the minister.

   ....

   b. "If I were a man without a conscience, I might have found peace," said the reverend.

   ....

   c. "The people revere you and you have certainly worked well among them," said Hester.

   ....

   d. "You have a friend in me," Hester said. (assure)

   ....

   e. "I have always been truthful, but in this circumstance I had no choice," she said. (assure)

   ....

   f. "Oh, Arthur," she cried, "forgive me!" (beg)

   ....

   g. "You will not go alone," she whispered.

   ....

None, no one, nothing, nowhere, no

These are all negative words often used at the beginning of a sentence or alone. Look at this example:

"Hester, have you found peace?"
*"**None – nothing** but despair."*

3 **Answer the questions using the words in brackets.**

   a. How many souvenirs did you buy?
   .... because I had .... money left.
   (no, none, nothing, no one)

   b. Where did he go on holiday?
   .... because he was feeling ill.
   (none, nothing, nowhere, no one)

   c. Was the play good?
   .... of us enjoyed the play. There was ....
   entertaining about it.
   (nothing, nowhere, none, no one)

   d. Where did they go all morning?
   ....! They got lost in the Underground and
   .... of them spoke English.
   (none, nowhere, nothing, no one)

   e. What did you find in her bag?
   .... because the thief had already stolen everything
   and he was .... to be found.
   (no one, nowhere, none, nothing)

   f. How many theater tickets are left?
   .... because they were sold out this morning, and
   .... knows if there will be another performance
   this week.
   (nothing, none, nowhere, no one)

Themes for thought, discussion and writing

Throughout the story, the devil, the Black Man, or Satan is a silent character. He is mentioned very often, with different names.

The Puritans acknowledged his presence as they acknowledged the presence of God. They attributed all misfortunes, tragedies, sins, curses and evil-doings to Satan.

Hawthorne wrote several short stories about the presence of evil and the devil in the lives of his protagonists.

4 **In what way is the devil "connected" with the following characters?**

Hester ....

Pearl ....

Reverend Dimmesdale ....

Roger Chillingworth ....

Mrs Hibbins ....

During the meeting in the forest, Hester again shows her courage and strength of character. After revealing Chillingworth's true identity to the shocked reverend, she is able to comfort and counsel him!

Reverend Dimmesdale says, "Think for me, Hester! You are strong. Resolve this for me!... Tell me what I must do. You are strong, Hester."

The reverend is obviously very insecure and frightened.

At the end of the chapter, he admits, "I have no strength or courage... to venture into... world alone."

Here he openly admits that he depends on Hester's strength and courage in order to live.

5 **Everyone, no matter how strong, has a weak point. What do you think Hester's weak point is? What is your weak point?**

CHAPTER **ELEVEN**

A Flood of Sunshine

1 Arthur Dimmesdale gazed into Hester's face with a look of hope and joy, mixed with fear. Hester was strong and determined. The scarlet letter had isolated her; it had made her an outsider. In a sense, it had freed her. As an outsider, she was free to see and judge the Puritan institutions and laws with a critical eye. Her mind was free to think, to wander, to dream. She had become very independent.

2 The minister, on the other hand, had lived and worked within the strict laws of the Puritan community. Only once had he transgressed [1] — but it had been a sin of passion, not of principle or purpose.

Finally, he was able to see a ray of hope in his future. He had

1. **transgressed** : broke a law or moral rule.

decided to flee, but not alone. He understood that he could no longer live without Hester's companionship, strength and tenderness. Once the decision had been made, he began to feel a strange enjoyment, a sense of exhilaration [1] and relief.

"You will go!" said Hester firmly. "Let us not look back. The past is gone. See! I am removing this symbol forever!"

Hester removed the scarlet letter and threw it away among the leaves.

The stigma was gone. Hester had not known its weight until she felt the freedom! Then she took off her cap and let her beautiful hair fall upon her shoulders. A tender smile appeared on her lips. Her sex, her youth and her beauty all came back from the past. And all at once, the sunshine burst forth into the dark forest.

(3) "And now, you must know Pearl!" she said joyfully. "Our little Pearl."

"Do you think she will be glad to know me?" he asked.

"She will love you dearly, and you will love her. I will call her! Pearl! Pearl!"

Pearl walked towards them. At a certain point, she stopped at the brook.

"Come little Pearl! Cross the brook!" said Hester gently.

Pearl did not want to go to her mother. She looked at Hester, and seemed to be searching for the scarlet letter on her bosom. She pointed her little finger at her mother's breast — the scarlet letter was missing! She shrieked wildly, gesticulated [2] violently and threw her small figure into extravagant contortions. Her anger seemed uncontrollable.

"I know what bothers her," whispered Hester to the clergyman. "Pearl misses something that I always wear. I must bear its torture

1. **exhilaration** : happiness and excitement.
2. **gesticulated** : made movements with one's hands to emphasize what one is saying.

The Scarlet Letter

a little longer until we have left this region. Then I will throw it into the ocean!"

With these words, she picked up the scarlet letter and fastened it to her bosom. She then gathered up her hair and put on her cap.

"Do you know your mother now?" Hester asked.

"Yes, now I will come," answered Pearl, jumping across the brook.

"Come, the minister wants to welcome you," said Hester. "He loves you, and he loves your mother too."

"Does he love us?" asked Pearl. "Will he go back with us, hand in hand, we three together?"

"Not now, dear child, but in a few days he will walk hand in hand with us. We will have a home and fireside of our own. You shall sit on his knee and he will teach you many things," Hester said.

The reverend, wanting to enter into the child's heart, bent forward and kissed her on the brow. Pearl immediately broke away and went to the brook, where she washed off the reverend's kiss.

(4) As the minister departed, he turned around to look at the mother and child to assure himself that he had not had a vision. He saw Hester in her gray dress and near her, little Pearl.

They had decided to flee to the Old World with its crowds and cities. There they would find a shelter and a civilization that were congenial [1] to the clergyman's culture.

It so happened that there was a ship in Boston harbor, that was sailing for Bristol [2] in four days. They booked the passage for two

---

1. **congenial** : pleasant in a way that makes one feel comfortable.
2. **Bristol** : English seaport.

A Flood of Sunshine

adults and a child. In three days, the minister had to deliver the important Election Sermon. He would not have left without doing his public duty.

After having met Hester in the forest, he felt a surge [1] of physical energy. He was amazed at the change that had taken place in his body and in his spirit. He felt strong, energetic and strangely mischievous. He felt transformed. At every step, he was tempted to do something wild or wicked. He had a strange desire to be scornful and bitter, to ridicule all that was good and holy. He felt spiteful [2] and unkind.

"What is it that haunts and tempts me in this way?" he said to himself. "Am I mad, or did I make a contract with the fiend of the forest and sign it with my blood?"

As he walked through the town, he met Mistress Hibbins who said, "So, Reverend sir, you have been to the forest. The next time, tell me and I will accompany you."

"The only reason I went to the forest was to greet my pious Indian friend, Apostle Eliot," [3] answered the reverend.

"Ha, ha, ha," cackled [4] the old witch-lady, and went away smiling.

The reverend hurried home and began working on the Election Sermon, which was extremely important to him.

There was a knock at the door. It was Roger Chillingworth.

"Welcome home, Reverend sir," he said. "How is Apostle

---

1. **surge** : sudden strong feeling.
2. **spiteful** : behaving in an unkind way to hurt or upset.
3. **Apostle Eliot** : converted Indian who appears in Boston history books.
4. **cackled** : gave a short, high laugh.

Eliot? Oh, but you are pale. My medicine will help you feel better for the Election Sermon."

"No, no! I do not think so. My walk in the forest and the clean air have done me good. I will not be needing your medicine any more, my friend."

All this time, Chillingworth was looking at the minister with the caring look of a physician. But in spite of this outward show, the reverend was almost convinced that the old man knew about his meeting with Hester.

The physician knew from the minister's look that he was no longer considered a friend, but a bitter enemy. Both of them carefully avoided the subject.

When the reverend was finally alone, a servant of the house brought him dinner, which he ate with a good appetite. Then he threw the original Election Sermon in the fire and began writing another one.

6　　On the day on which the new governor of Boston was to take office, Hester and Pearl came to the marketplace. It was an important holiday because it marked the beginning of the new political year of the colony.

The marketplace was crowded with the inhabitants of Boston, dressed in their black and gray clothes. There were also brightly dressed Indians, settlers from the wilderness and rough-looking sailors from the ship that was in the harbor. The Puritans were a bit less stern and gloomy [1] on this holiday. Hester finally felt free, happy and hopeful. She knew that soon she would be starting a new life without the scarlet letter. Her heart was light.

---

1. **gloomy** : dark, pessimistic, sad.

A Flood of Sunshine

In the distance, Hester could see Chillingworth talking to the commander of the ship. After a while, the commander stopped to speak to Hester.

"Well, Mistress Prynne, I have another passenger on board my ship! This time we will have two doctors on board — the ship's surgeon and this other doctor."

"What do you mean," asked Hester, who was startled. [1] "Is there another passenger?"

"Why, you must know! This physician, this Chillingworth, says he is a member of your party, and a close friend of the gentleman you spoke of."

"They know each other well, indeed," replied Hester, trying to be calm.

At that instant, she saw old Chillingworth himself, standing at the corner of the marketplace, smiling at her wickedly.

Before Hester could collect her thoughts, the sound of military music was approaching. The procession of magistrates and citizens was on its way to the meetinghouse, where Reverend Dimmesdale would deliver the Election Sermon.

The music became louder and Pearl clapped her hands. Following the magistrates, came the young and eminently [2] divine reverend, who would preach the sermon. This was the first time that Reverend Dimmesdale had shown such energy during a procession. His body was not bent and his hand did not rest on his heart. But it was a spiritual strength, not a physical one.

Hester gazed at the clergyman, and felt that he was another person, so different from the reverend she had met in the forest.

1. **startled** : very surprised, astonished, shocked.
2. **eminently** : obviously, outstandingly.

The Scarlet Letter

She hardly knew him! He moved proudly on, surrounded by the rich music and the procession of the venerable leaders.

Hester decided to listen to the sermon from her position beside the scaffold since the meetinghouse was very crowded. The reverend's voice was like a musical instrument. It was filled with emotion, passion and anguish. It was majestic, but there was an element of sadness in it.

As Hester listened to the sounds that came from the meetinghouse, Pearl ran about the marketplace, looking at the townspeople, the Indians and the sailors.

One of the sailors said to her, "Your mother is that woman with the scarlet letter. Tell her that I send this message: I spoke again to the old doctor, and he will arrange to bring his friend, the man she knows, aboard with him. So your mother need not worry, except for herself and you. Go and tell your mother!"

Pearl nodded and ran off to tell her mother, who was devastated [1] by this message. Was there no way out of this labyrinth [2] of misery and persecution?

---

1. **devastated** : shocked and upset.
2. **labyrinth** : a confusing set of paths.

Comprehension

FCE ❶ Read the text below and decide which answer, A, B, C or D, best fits each space.

The scarlet letter had (**1**) .... Hester and she had (**2**) .... very independent. Reverend Dimmesdale had decided to (**3**) ...., but not alone. He knew he could no (**4**) .... live without Hester's companionship and strength. Hester took (**5**) .... the scarlet letter and threw it (**6**) .... the leaves of the forest. She let her hair (**7**) .... and her beauty came back.

When Pearl returned she did not see the scarlet letter on Hester's (**8**) .... and she shrieked wildly. Hester put it on and Pearl jumped (**9**) .... the brook. Reverend Dimmesdale kissed Pearl on the forehead but she immediately broke (**10**) .... and went to the brook and washed off his kiss.

1.	**A** exiled	**B** deserted	**C** detached	**D** isolated
2.	**A** become	**B** became	**C** becomes	**D** becoming
3.	**A** run	**B** flee	**C** move	**D** go
4.	**A** length	**B** longest	**C** longer	**D** long
5.	**A** out	**B** off	**C** of	**D** on
6.	**A** up	**B** at	**C** by	**D** among
7.	**A** down	**B** on	**C** under	**D** in
8.	**A** body	**B** bosom	**C** shoulder	**D** front
9.	**A** away	**B** on	**C** across	**D** up
10.	**A** out	**B** away	**C** in	**D** by

FCE 2 Read the text below. Use the word in capitals at the end of each line to form a word that fits in the space in the same line.

The scarlet letter had isolated Hester and it had
(**1**) .... her.   FREE

Reverend Dimmesdale admired and needed Hester's
(**2**) .... to change his life. Once the decision   STRONG
to flee had been taken he felt a strange (**3**) ....   ENJOY
and relief.

He suddenly felt (**4**) .... and strong. He had a   ENERGY
strange desire to be (**5**) .... and unkind. He went   SCORN
home and worked on the Election Sermon which was
(**6**) .... important to him.   EXTREME

Hester felt happy and (**7**) .... because she knew she   HOPE
would soon be starting a new life without the scarlet letter.

But she was (**8**) .... when she found out that   STARTLE
Chillingworth had also booked a passage on the same ship.
The presence of Chillingworth was a (**9**) ....,   PERSECUTE
and she did not have a (**10**) ....   SOLVE

FCE 3 Chapter Eleven has been divided into seven parts. Choose from the list A-H the sentence which best summarizes each part (1-7) of the chapter. There is one heading which you do not need to use.

A ☐ Meeting the child

B ☐ Bad news

C ☐ Being an outsider

D ☐ An amazing change

E ☐ The sermon

F ☐ Bitter enemies

G ☐ Revenge

H ☐ Leaving the past behind

Grammar

Phrasal verbs with "look"

4 **A Here are some phrasal verbs with the verb "look ". Match them with their meanings.**

1. ☐ look forward to something	**a.**	to seek information about someone or something
2. ☐ look someone or something over	**b.**	to take care of someone or something
3. ☐ look someone or something up	**c.**	to view someone or something as inferior
4. ☐ look after someone or something	**d.**	to anticipate something with enthusiasm
5. ☐ look down on someone or something	**e.**	to examine someone or something
6. ☐ look alike	**f.**	to appear similar

B Now fill in the gaps with the correct phrasal verb.

a. The master .... the servants and treated them badly.

b. Before giving this essay to the teacher, ... carefully for spelling errors!

c. It's very difficult to distinguish identical twins because they ....

d. The young mother could not leave the house since she had to .... the sick baby.

e. I forgot their telephone number. I must .... in the telephone directory.

f. It had been a difficult year and the students really .... the summer holidays.

Themes for thought, discussion and writing

5 The decision to flee together transformed both Hester and Dimmesdale. Their physical and psychological changes were almost immediate. List their changes in this table.

	Hester	Reverend Dimmesdale
Psychological Changes		
Physical Changes		

6 The power of the mind over the body is amazing. Scientists have studied this for years and continue to do so with interesting results. Have you personally experienced the power of the mind over the body?

If so, please explain. ....

....

....

....

If not, do you know of someone who has? ....

....

....

....

7 Psychosomatic illnesses are bodily ailments that are caused or aggravated by a mental or emotional disorder.
Can you think of some common illnesses that can be psychosomatic? Two are listed for you.

ulcer ....

headache ....

....

....

....

....

....

....

....

T: GRADE 8

8 TOPIC – THE SUPERNATURAL
There are many references to the supernatural in *The Scarlet Letter.* Find a picture which illustrates or has some connection with the supernatural. Bring it to your friend(s) and talk about it mentioning the following points:

a. What is happening in the picture?

b. Is it taken from real life or is it an imaginary picture?

c. Has anything "supernatural" ever happened to you?

d. Are supernatural phenomena only evil or can they also be good?

e. People have been having visions for centuries. Do you think there could be a plausible scientific explanation for them?

CHAPTER **TWELVE**

The Revelation of the Scarlet Letter

The eloquent sermon came to an end. The enraptured [1] listeners left the church and in the open air began praising the minister. According to them, no man had ever spoken so wisely, no man had ever been so pious. To them, he was a saint. He was enjoying his moment of glory, while Hester was standing beside the scaffold with the scarlet letter still burning on her breast.

As the military men and magistrates moved onward, all eyes turned to the minister. How weak and pale he looked in the

---

1. **enraptured** : filled with joy, delight.

middle of his triumph! The inspiration that had sustained him during his sermon had left him now that he had performed his duty. He tried to walk on, but he could barely stand erect.

The crowd looked on in awe [1] and wonder. He passed near the scaffold where, years ago, Hester had been shamed. He paused, turned toward the scaffold and stretched out his arms.

"Hester," he said, "come here! Come, my little Pearl!" His aspect was ghastly. The child ran to him and clasped her arms around his knees. Hester went near him slowly against her will. [2] At that instant, Chillingworth pushed through the crowd to snatch [3] back his victim. He caught the minister's arm and said,

"Madman, stop! Send away that woman and this child. Do not blacken your fame and perish in dishonor! I can still save you!"

"Ha, tempter! You are too late!" answered the minister. "With God's help, I will escape you now!"

He again extended his hand to the woman with the scarlet letter.

"Hester Prynne," he cried, with piercing earnestness, "in the name of God, who gave me the grace to do what I did not do seven years ago, come here now! Give me strength, Hester!"

The crowd saw the minister, leaning on Hester's shoulder and supported by her arm around him, ascend [4] the steps of the scaffold. Roger Chillingworth followed them and said, "There is no place on earth where you could have escaped me except on this scaffold!"

The reverend trembled, turned to Hester and said, "Isn't this better than what we dreamed of in the forest?"

"I don't know! I don't know!" she replied hurriedly. "Better? Yes, so that we may both die, and little Pearl die with us!"

---

1. **awe** : admiration, reverence.
2. **against her will** : unwillingly, she didn't want to go.
3. **snatch** : pull, take.
4. **ascend** : move up.

"For you and Pearl, God is merciful. Now, let me do what I must. Hester, I am a dying man. So let me take my shame upon myself."

Supported in part by Hester, and holding one of Pearl's hands, the Reverend Dimmesdale turned to the rulers, the ministers and the people. They all knew that an important event of his life was about to be revealed to them.

"People of New England!" he cried with a high, solemn voice. "You who have loved me, you who have considered me holy, look at me here, a sinner of the world. At last, I stand upon the spot where, seven years ago, I should have stood with this woman who now sustains [1] me. You have all shuddered at the scarlet letter that Hester wears. But there was a person among you whose sin you did not know!"

The minister fought against his bodily weakness. He stepped passionately forward and said, "It was on him! God's eye saw it! The angels were always pointing to it! The Devil knew it well! But he hid it from his fellow men. Now at this hour of death, he stands up before you. He asks you to look again at Hester Prynne's scarlet letter! He tells you, that with all its mysterious horror, it is but the shadow of what he bears on his own breast."

With a convulsive motion, he tore away the ministerial band from his breast. It was revealed! But it is irreverent to describe that revelation. For an instant, the gaze of the horror-stricken [2] crowd was concentrated on the ghastly miracle. There was a flush of triumph on his face. Then he sank down on the scaffold. Hester supported his head against her bosom. Old Chillingworth knelt down beside him.

"You have escaped me," he repeated more than once.

"May God forgive you," said the minister. "You, too, have deeply sinned."

1. **sustains** : makes one feel strong and hopeful.
2. **horror-stricken** : shocked, filled with horror.

The Revelation of the Scarlet Letter

He turned to the woman and the child.

"My little Pearl," he said weakly, with a serene [1] smile on his face, "will you kiss me now? You did not want to kiss me in the forest."

Pearl kissed his lips. A spell was broken.

"Hester," said the clergyman, "farewell!"

"Will we not meet again?" she whispered. "Will we not spend our immortal life together? Surely we have paid for our sin!"

"Hush, [2] Hester, hush!" he said. "We broke the law. We forgot our God. It is therefore vain to hope that we can meet hereafter in an everlasting and pure reunion. God knows and He is merciful. He has proved his mercy in my afflictions. He brought me here to die this death of triumphant ignominy before the people. Praised be his name! His will be done! Farewell!"

That final word came forth with the minister's last breath. The multitude broke out in a strange deep voice of fear and wonder.

There was more than one account of what had been witnessed on the scaffold. Most of the spectators testified to having seen on the breast of the unhappy minister, a SCARLET LETTER — the same as that worn by Hester Prynne and imprinted in the flesh.

There were several explanations regarding its origin. Some said that the reverend inflicted a hideous torture on himself. Others claimed that evil old Roger Chillingworth caused it to appear by giving the reverend poisonous and magic drugs. Others contended that the stigma was the effect of remorse and Heaven's dreadful judgment.

Certain persons, who were spectators of the whole scene, denied having seen any mark whatever on his breast. They also said that his dying words did not acknowledge the slightest

---

1. **serene** : peaceful and calm.
2. **hush** : Be quiet! Be silent!

connection, on his part, with Hester Prynne's scarlet letter. According to these witnesses, he wanted to teach them that, no matter how holy or pure, we are sinners all alike.

This version of Reverend Dimmesdale's story shows the stubborn loyalty with which a man's friend will uphold his character — even when there is clear proof that he is a false and sin-stained creature of the dust.

Within the year, old Roger Chillingworth, having lost his only purpose in life, withered up [1] and died. In his last will and testament he left a considerable amount of property, both in the New World and in England, to Pearl.

So Pearl — the demon offspring, the elf-child — became the richest heiress of her day in the New World.

After the physician's death, Hester and Pearl disappeared and no one knew where they had gone. Many years passed and one day a tall woman in a gray robe approached the cottage by the seashore, where Hester had lived. It had never been opened in all those years. The woman, with a scarlet letter on her breast, entered the cottage. Hester Prynne had returned.

But where was Pearl? No one ever knew. But through the remainder of Hester's life, there were indications that she was the object of love and interest of an inhabitant of another land. Letters with armorial seals arrived. In the cottage there were articles of comfort and luxury that Hester had never used, which only wealth could have purchased. Once, Hester was seen embroidering a baby garment with lavish [2] richness.

---

1. **withered up** : dried up, decreased in size, faded.
2. **lavish** : more than enough, excessive.

The Revelation of the Scarlet Letter

Gossips of that day tell us that Pearl was not only alive, but married, happy and always mindful [1] of her mother.

Hester had preferred to return to Boston rather than remain in that unknown region where Pearl had found a home. There was a more real life for her here. This was the place of her sin, her sorrow and her penance. She wore the scarlet letter of her own free will. The scarlet letter ceased to be a stigma and was looked upon with awe and reverence.

Hester lived unselfishly and devoted her life to comforting and counseling women who were burdened with sorrow, sin and suffering.

Women came to her asking why they were so wretched, [2] and what could be done to relieve their troubles. Hester assured them that one day there would be a drastic transformation in society. The whole relationship between men and women would change, bringing greater justice and happiness.

After many, many years a new grave was dug near an old, sunken one in the burial ground beside the King's Chapel. There was a space between them, as if the dust of the two sleepers had no right to mingle. [3] One tombstone served for both. On this simple slab of slate, there appeared an engraved coat of arms. It had this inscription, [4] that might serve as a motto and brief description of our legend:

ON A FIELD, SABLE, [5] THE LETTER A, GULES. [6]

---

1. **mindful** : giving thought or careful attention, not forgetful.
2. **wretched** : very unhappy, depressed, hopeless.
3. **mingle** : mix, unite.
4. **inscription** : words that written or cut in something.
5. **sable** : black.
6. **gules** : red.

Comprehension

1 **Answer the following questions.**

a. What did Reverend Dimmesdale do as he passed near the scaffold?

b. How did Roger Chillingworth react?

c. What did the reverend tell the people of New England?

d. What was the "ghastly miracle" and how was it interpreted by the townspeople?

e. Where did Hester and Pearl go after Chillingworth's death?

f. According to the gossips of that day, what happened to Pearl?

g. Why did Hester return to Boston, and what was the purpose of her life there?

2 **Complete the following summary by filling in the blank spaces. The first letter of the correct word is given to help you.**

After the triumphant (1) E.................. Sermon, the reverend became very (2) W.................. and he could (3) b.................. walk.

He (4) s.................. by the scaffold and (5) s.................. out his (6) a.................. to Hester and Pearl, (7) c.................. them by name.

Although Chillingworth (8) t.................. to stop him, the reverend, who was a (9) d.................. man, decided to (10) c.................. to the (11) t.................. of Boston that he was the (12) f.................. of Hester's (13) c.................. .

In his (14) p.................. confession, he (15) t.................. away the ministerial (16) b.................. from his (17) b.................., and revealed a (18) s.................. !.................. imprinted in his (19) f.................. . The crowd was (20) h.................. – s.................. .

After the reverend's (21) d.................. Chillingworth (22) w.................. up and died. Hester and Pearl went (23) a.................. for many years.

However, after a long (24) a.................. Hester returned to (25) B.................. of her own (26) f.................. will. She lived a

(**27**) I..................... entirely devoted to (**28**) h.................... and
(**29**) C.................. wretched (**30**) W.................... . All through her
(**31**) I..................., Pearl remembered Hester with letters and expensive
(**32**) g.................. .

Hester was (**33**) b.................... at the Kings (**34**) C..................
near an old (**35**) g.................. . The (**36**) I.................... on the
(**37**) t.................. served for both graves. It read: ON A FIELD,
(**38**) S.................. , The Letter A, (**39**) g.................. .

Grammar

Verbs with "-ing" clauses

Look at these sentences from Chapter 12:
*The enraptured listeners left the church and in the open air **began praising** the minister.*
*Certain persons **denied having** seen any mark whatever on his breast.*

Many verbs are followed by an "-ing" clause. The subject of the verb is also the subject of the "-ing" clause. The most common of these verbs are:

- verbs of saying and thinking:

admit   consider   describe   suggest   deny
mention   imagine   remember

e.g. *We **suggested taking** a walk.*

- verbs of like and dislike:

adore   hate   enjoy   mind   dread   love
dislike   resent   detest

e.g. *She **enjoys visiting** her daughter.*

- other common verbs:

begin   finish   avoid   risk   keep
start   stop   practice   resist   continue

e.g. *They will **continue playing** until midday.*

3 **A** Rewrite the following sentences using an "-ing" clause instead of a reported clause.

     a. He did not admit that he had spoken to the witch.

     b. I suggested that we give her monetary help.

     c. Hester remembered that she had gone to the forest alone.

B Now complete these dialogues using the words in the box and another suitable verb.

start	dread	adore	risk	avoid

     a. **A.** Tomorrow is the first day of school.
         B. Oh, no! I .... back!

     b. **A.** Your grandparents go to concerts every weekend.
         B. Yes, they .... to music.

     c. **A.** Why did they take the back road?
         B. They wanted to .... on the noisy street.

     d. **A.** Why are you in such a rush?
         B. It's already eight o'clock and I can't .... late for work.

     e. **A.** What are you doing now?
         B. I should .... for my exam.

Writing

4 You have just witnessed Reverend Dimmesdale's "confession" and death on the scaffold. You must write a newspaper article in 120-180 words about what you have seen. Use the information given in the story and include the following details:

- the success of the Election Sermon
- Reverend Dimmesdale's physical condition

- what Reverend Dimmesdale said on the scaffold
- the reactions of Hester and Chillingworth
- what Dimmesdale revealed to the townspeople
- what some townspeople saw on Dimmesdale's breast

Start like this:

THE BOSTON GAZETTE

Yesterday the new Governor of Boston took office and it was an important holiday. At the meeting-house ....

Find a suitable headline for your article.

Themes for thought, discussion and writing

5 Why did the reverend decide to give a public confession and not flee?

6 Why did he speak in the third person?

7 Do you think it took courage to do what he did? Why?

8 It is often said that people see what they want to see. Many townspeople insisted that there was no scarlet letter on Dimmesdale's breast, and that his public confession did not refer to him.
How can you explain this?

9 Hawthorne writes that "having lost his only purpose in life, [Chillingworth] withered up and died." The term "withered up" is usually used for plants or flowers, not people.
Why was this term used?

10 Hester's inner rebellion and free thinking became her crusade in her later years. She was almost a prophetess of the deep social change that was about to happen in the United States, regarding the rights of women and minorities.
What other women in history have fought to better things?

11 Have women achieved equal rights in your society? Why or why not?

12 What should be changed and why?

13 The film *The Scarlet Letter*, starring Demi Moore, Gary Oldman and Robert Duvall, was based on Hawthorne's novel.
Many things were changed in the film; a few things remained the same. In the following table, list the changes and the things that remained the same.

Things that changed	Things that were the same

14 The letter A can stand for many words. What "A" words can you think of that describe Hester Prynne? Why?

....

....

....

The Importance of *The Scarlet Letter* in American Literature

The Scarlet Letter is a rarity in nineteenth-century American literature because a woman is the heroine of the story.

Hester Prynne is a very different type of heroine. She is a strong, determined woman. She is rebellious and refuses authority. Her suffering, her punishment and social isolation make her a bold, independent individual.

Hester is truly the author of her own destiny. She left the prison and walked to the scaffold of her own free will. She bravely decided to remain in Boston, even though she could have fled. She made the decision for herself and the reverend to flee together to Europe. Once she had succeeded in giving Pearl a better life than her own, she returned to Boston of *her own free will* – and she wore the scarlet letter again because she wanted to do so.

Her decisions reflected great individuality and independence. In a way, she represented what America would one day become.

Hawthorne's novel is full of allegories. [1] Hester, who comes from England, represents the new colonial mentality that is desperately trying to break away from Old World traditions.

Pearl, who is born in the New World, is a symbol of the American future. Hawthorne writes that Pearl is "wild and majestic". When she is examined by Reverend Wilson, she is not at all intimidated by his authority. She is openly mischievous in front of him: she puts

---

1. **allegories** : symbolic representations; stories in which the characters and actions represent good and bad qualities.

her finger in her mouth, refuses to speak, and then gives him a "pagan" answer, asserting that she was picked from a wild rose bush. Pearl represents what Hester desperately fought to be: a strong, independent, open-minded American woman of the future.

Reverend Dimmesdale symbolizes many things. In particular, he represents the hypocrisy behind many authoritative institutions, such as religion.

In the reverend, we see that the real key to his character is not religious piety, but his dependence on the good opinion of society. While Dimmesdale enjoyed admiration, devotion and prestige, he was hiding a hideous secret that caused two other people to suffer. He never doubted that what he and Hester did in the past was evil. He never doubted that he deserved to be punished. But to actually confess his act and receive his punishment, would mean to lose his position in society, which he could not live without.

The reverend's sermon was a masterpiece of double-talk. He often "confessed" publicly on the pulpit, always using symbolic language which he knew would be misunderstood by his congregation. These actions not only relieved his guilt by "revealing" the truth, but also made him appear even more holy, humble and pious in the eyes of his devoted listeners.

All through his life, Hawthorne had an interior conflict between his respect for the past, and his great abhorrence [1] of the Puritan cruelty and narrow-mindedness. He never forgot his ancestor, the notorious Judge John Hathorne, who presided at the Salem witch trials. Nathaniel Hawthorne was not a church-going man.

Roger Chillingworth is the extreme representation of a pitiless

---

1. **abhorrence** : hatred.

conscience. He is obsessed by vengeance and loses all human qualities. As Hawthorne writes, "Chillingworth was a striking evidence of a man's faculty [1] of transforming himself into a devil". This learned scholar and scientist became the victim of his own obsessions.

Considering that Hawthorne wrote this novel in 1849, his ability as a psychologist was remarkable. He created complex characters that reflected the many facets [2] of the human mind – characters that struggled with the timeless themes of love, sex, sin, evil, punishment, rebellion, hypocrisy, revenge and hate.

The famous American writer Henry James described *The Scarlet Letter* as "the finest piece of imaginative writing yet put forth in this country".

A scene from the film version of *The Scarlet letter.*

---

1. **faculty** : ability.

2. **facets** : aspects, parts.

1 Choose the correct answer.

1. *The Scarlet Letter* is a rarity in nineteenth-century American literature because

   A ☐ it deals with adultery.

   B ☐ a woman is the heroine.

   C ☐ it indirectly criticizes the Puritans.

2. In a sense, Hester represents

   A ☐ what America would one day become.

   B ☐ the Puritan concept of sin and punishment.

   C ☐ all Puritan women.

3. Hawthorne describes Pearl as

   A ☐ afraid of religious leaders.

   B ☐ openly disobedient.

   C ☐ wild and majestic.

4. The most important thing for Reverend Dimmesdale was

   A ☐ his religious duty.

   B ☐ his love for Hester.

   C ☐ the good opinion of society.

5. When he spoke of his sin on the pulpit,

   A ☐ he used symbolic language which was misunderstood.

   B ☐ he trembled and then fainted.

   C ☐ everyone believed him.

6. Chillingworth's obsessive vengeance

   A ☐ transformed him into a devil.

   B ☐ transformed him into a scientist.

   C ☐ made him join the devil worshippers.

EXIT TEST

FCE **①** **Choose the answer, A, B, C or D, which you think fits best according to the text.**

1. Most of the women of the town

   A ☐ did not want Hester to be punished.

   B ☐ wanted Hester to leave Boston.

   C ☐ wanted Hester to receive a more severe punishment.

   D ☐ wanted Hester to go to the pillory.

2. Roger Chillingworth saw his wife for the first time

   A ☐ at Governor Bellingham's mansion.

   B ☐ in prison.

   C ☐ on the pillory.

   D ☐ on the scaffold.

3. Roger Chillingworth made Hester

   A ☐ keep the secret of his identity.

   B ☐ tell Dimmesdale his true identity.

   C ☐ wear the scarlet letter.

   D ☐ leave Boston forever.

4. Hester chose to live in the Puritan settlement

   A ☐ but she could not work in the community.

   B ☐ but she was completely isolated.

   C ☐ and she made friends with the poor of the community.

   D ☐ and Pearl made friends with the other children in Boston.

5. Governor Bellingham
   A ☐ wanted Pearl to live with his family.
   B ☐ wanted Hester and Pearl to leave Boston.
   C ☐ thought Pearl was a living sin.
   D ☐ did not think Hester could raise her child in a Christian manner.

6. There had been a remarkable change for the worse in Chillingworth's aspect because
   A ☐ he was very old.
   B ☐ there was something ugly and evil in his face.
   C ☐ he worked long hours.
   D ☐ he was ill.

7. Reverend Dimmesdale was a tormented man because
   A ☐ he was filled with remorse and cowardice.
   B ☐ he was very ill.
   C ☐ he wanted to marry Hester.
   D ☐ his congregation did not like his sermons.

8. Chillingworth had transformed himself into
   A ☐ a holy man.
   B ☐ a minister of the church.
   C ☐ a devil.
   D ☐ a town leader.

9. Reverend Dimmesdale became very angry with Hester
   A ☐ because she did not want to marry him.
   B ☐ when she called him a hypocrite.
   C ☐ because she did not go to church regularly.
   D ☐ when she revealed Chillingworth's true identity.

10. Hester and Reverend Dimmesdale decided
   A ☐ to take off the scarlet letter forever.
   B ☐ to flee to Europe together with Pearl.
   C ☐ never to meet again.
   D ☐ to talk to Chillingworth together. \

11. When Dimmesdale was on the scaffold, most of the townspeople thought they saw
   A ☐ an infernal light in his eyes.
   B ☐ tears in his eyes.
   C ☐ a scarlet letter imprinted in his flesh.
   D ☐ a red mark on his forehead.

12. During the last years of her life, Hester
   A ☐ lived the life of a rich woman.
   B ☐ returned to her parents' town in England.
   C ☐ taught catechism at the Boston meetinghouse.
   D ☐ devoted her life to comforting women who suffered.

FCE ② **Who did what?**
For questions 1.-14. choose from the people (A-H).

A = Gov. Bellingham   **E** = Hester
B = Reverend Wilson   **F** = Pearl
C = Reverend Dimmesdale   **G** = Mistress Hibbins
D = Roger Chillingworth   **H** = Town-beadle

She was the governor's bad-tempered sister who
was later executed as a witch.   1. ....
He was the oldest clergyman in Boston.   2. ....

Her mother made her elaborate dresses.	**3.** ....
She was very skilled with the needle.	**4.** ....
He opened the prison door when Hester went to the scaffold.	**5.** ....
He was considered a saint by his congregation.	**6.** ....
He was born with a physical deformity.	**7.** ....
He was the head of the Boston community.	**8.** ....
Her beauty was flawless.	**9.** ....
She was a Sister of Mercy.	**10.** ....
She became a very rich heiress in the New World.	**11.** ....
He died on the scaffold.	**12.** ....
He had become an evil fiend.	**13.** ....
He wrote the Election Sermon.	**14.** ....

3 **Match the word with its meaning.**

1. ☐ surge		**a.**	behaving in an unkind way
2. ☐ enraptured		**b.**	very surprised, shocked
3. ☐ spiteful		**c.**	suspicious, cautious
4. ☐ meddle		**d.**	dark, pessimistic, sad
5. ☐ startled		**e.**	honest, responsible
6. ☐ ailment		**f.**	not healthy, weak
7. ☐ gloomy		**g.**	sudden strong feeling
8. ☐ upright		**h.**	filled with joy, delight
9. ☐ wary		**i.**	illness
10. ☐ sickly		**j.**	interfere

CONTEXT

4 **Answer the following questions.**

    a. Who wrote *The Scarlet Letter* ?

    b. Where and when was he born?

    c. What do you remember about his life?

    d. Briefly describe the Puritans and their beliefs.

    e. What is the Calvinist work ethic and how has it influenced life in the United States?

    f. What were the Salem Witch Trials and when did they take place?

COMPREHENSION

5 **Decide if the following sentences are true or false and then correct the false ones.**

	T	F
a. When Hester stood on the scaffold at the beginning of the story, her child was about 3 years old.		
b. She was made to wear the letter "A" on her dress.		
c. Hester revealed the name of her lover.		
d. Chillingworth wanted to punish Hester for her betrayal.		
e. Hester was very popular in the Puritan community.		
f. Reverend Wilson wanted to take Pearl away from Hester.		
g. Roger Chillingworth went to live with Reverend Dimmesdale.		
h. Chillingworth became obsessed with Hester.		
i. Hester and Dimmesdale decided to leave the Puritan community together.		
j. Chillingworth discovered their plans to leave.		
k. Hester and Dimmesdale started a new life in England.		

WHO SAID IT?

a. "God gave her the child and the instinctive knowledge of its nature and needs, which no other mortal can possess."

b. "Is there death in this cup?"

c. "Between you and me the scale hangs fairly balanced."

d. "Will he go back with us, hand in hand, we three together?"

e. "This is her way of laughing at the magistrates, and making the punishment something to be proud of."

f. "Come along, Madame Hester, and show your scarlet letter in the marketplace!"

g. "I found them growing on a grave that had no tombstone."

h. "The human heart hides our most hideous secrets, and it must do so until that Last Day."

i. "Be it a sin or not, I hate that man."

j. "Will we not spend our immortal life together?"

The Scarlet Letter

KEY TO THE ACTIVITIES AND EXIT TEST

Hawthorne and *The Scarlet Letter*

Page 14 – exercise 1

a. False – A family living in Colorado discovered a notebook, kept by Nathaniel Hawthorne, with a collection of words and ideas for his future masterpiece, *The Scarlet Letter*.
b. False – It was a collection of words, fragments of sentences and ideas.
c. True
d. True
e. False – While working at the Customhouse in Salem, he found a mysterious package.
f. True
g. False – Surveyor Pue had written about the scarlet letter and its owner on several sheets of faded paper, which Hawthorne found in the mysterious package.
h. False – The story is about a woman who is condemned to wear the scarlet letter in the Puritan settlement of Boston, between 1642 and 1649.
i. True

Before reading

Page 15 – exercise 1

a. 6. **b.** 5. **c.** 8. **d.** 1. **e.** 7. **f.** 4.
g. 9. **h.** 2. **i.** 3

Page 16 – exercise 2

Open answer.

Page 16 – exercise 3

1. C **2.** A **3.** C **4.** B **5.** A

CHAPTER ONE

Page 20 – exercise 1

An atmosphere of gloom, sadness and severity.

Page 20 – exercise 2

Nouns	Adjectives
prison	weatherbeaten
burial ground	sinister
grave	ugly
age	gloomy
rust	condemned
weeds	dark
criminal	
doom	
frailty	
sorrow	

Page 20 – exercise 3

Black and gray, because in Western society they are the colors of death, mourning, old age, sadness, severity and poverty.

Page 20 – exercise 4

Yes, there are some rare kinds of flowers that are black, or that look black. Two examples are the black tulip and the rare black orchid. Because the two words are almost contradictory. When you think of a flower you think of a beautiful, cheerful color. The term "black flower" seems to be an anomaly, a mistake of nature, something ugly or evil; thus, a perfect description for a prison.

Page 20 – exercise 5

1. were surprised to find
2. was following the prisoner
3. must have been built
4. will have to have
5. had difficulty staying
6. wished he had never (not) gone
7. said not to pick

Page 21 – exercise 6

No, it isn't.

Page 21 – exercise 7

In some oriental countries, white is considered a color of death.

Page 21 – exercise 8

Suggested answers:

a. red: anger, danger, love, passion, leftist political tendencies
b. pink: femininity, birth of a baby girl
c. green: nature, ecology, hope, youth, life, envy
d. yellow: warning sign, jealousy
e. purple: royalty, bad luck color for actors and actresses of the theatre
f. black: death, mourning
g. white: purity, marriage, innocence, light
h. blue: birth of a baby boy, sea, holidays, water

CHAPTER TWO

Page 29 – exercise 1

a. They were waiting for Hester Prynne to leave the prison.
b. Because they thought Hester's punishment was not severe enough.
   One goodwife suggested putting the brand of a hot iron on Hester's forehead.
c. She was condemned to stand on the platform an entire morning for everyone to look at, and to wear the scarlet letter "A" all her life.
d. She remembered her childhood, her schooldays, her years as a young girl, her native village in England, her paternal home, her parents' faces and the pale face of a scholar.

Page 29 – exercise 2

Hester: elegant body, young, regular face, dark hair, black eyes, colorful complexion, marked brow, burning blush, tall, natural dignity, arrogant smile
Women in the crowd: hard features, severe, grim, bitter
Spectators: grim, solemn, severe, rigid
Town-Beadle: black shadow, grim, threatening

Page 30 – exercise 3

Open answer.

Page 31 – exercise 4

1. f. **2.** g. **3.** a. **4.** b. **5.** d. **6.** e. **7.** c

Page 31 – exercise 5

Open answer.
Possible answers:
Public punishment is generally announced to others and carried out for others to witness. This is obviously embarrassing and humiliating for the person involved.
Private punishment generally involves the few people concerned. It can also involve only the "guilty" individual and his/her conscience or God.

Page 31 – exercise 6

Open answer.
Possible answer:
Yes, countries in the Middle East and Asia; particularly the Islamic countries.

Page 31 – exercise 7

Hester's mind began thinking about her past and the events connected to it.

The Puritans – the Origins

Page 34 – exercise 1

a. False – Puritanism developed within the Church of England during the late 16th century.
b. True
c. False – Their religious beliefs influenced every aspect of their daily life.
d. True
e. False – The Massachusetts Bay Company was formed by the Puritans.
f. True
g. False – The Puritans landed in Salem and then founded Boston.

Page 35 – exercise 2

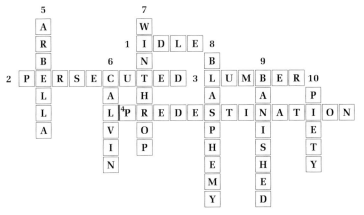

Page 36 – exercise 3

a. predestination: a person was either predestined by God for eternal salvation or eternal damnation.

b. the work ethic: success in the work world was seen as a sign of God's favor, and one's predestination to salvation. It is at the root of everyday life in America, where devotion to hard work and business enterprise is looked upon very favorably.

Page 36 – exercise 4

Possible answers:

Advantages	Disadvantages
a productive individual a productive society a strong economy general well-being opportunity to realize one's ambitions self-reliance high self-esteem personal discipline	risk of becoming too materialistic risk of neglecting free time and relaxation

Page 36 – exercises 5-8

Open answers.

Before reading

Page 37 – exercise 1

1. C 2. B 3. A 4. C 5. B

CHAPTER THREE

Page 44 – exercise 1

1. B 2. C 3. B 4. A 5. D 6. C

Page 45 – exercise 2

1. D 2. C 3. D 4. E 5. C 6. F 7. A
8. D 9. F 10. A 11. B 12. F

Page 46 – exercise 3

1. who 2. who 3. which 4. omit
5. who 6. omit 7. who 8. omit

Before reading

Page 47 – exercise 1

1. C 2. B 3. A 4. B 5. C

CHAPTER FOUR

Page 53 – exercise 1

a. She was in a state of nervous excitement.

b. He was staying in the prison as a guest, until the magistrates could meet with the Indians to decide his ransom.

c. She thought he would avenge himself on her and on her child, by giving them poison to drink.

d. It stopped crying and then fell asleep.

e. No, she hadn't.

f. Because they had both wronged each other. He knew he should never have married her because of his age and physical deformity; in this sense, he had wronged her.

g. He planned to devote himself to searching for him and finding him.

h. He did not want the dishonor of being the husband of a faithless woman and perhaps for other reasons.

i. She must not reveal Roger Chillingworth's real identity to anyone.

Page 53 – exercise 2

1. of   **2.** to   **3.** must/would   **4.** on
5. for   **6.** her   **7.** who   **8.** discover/find
9. against/on   **10.** his

Page 54 – exercise 3

a. Hester Prynne, who has just arrived from Amsterdam, is a new member of the community.
b. Boston, which is one of America's leading cities, is on the Atlantic coast.
c. Reverend Dimmesdale, whose behavior was ambiguous, became the most respected reverend of the settlement.
d. Nathaniel Hawthorne, who died in 1864, is considered one of America's greatest writers.
e. The new school, which is three miles away, will open in September.
f. The young man, whose sister is a teacher in Salem, is the new governor of Boston.

Page 55 – exercises 4-6

Open answers.

Religion in America

Page 59 – exercise 1

a. Christian
b. Spanish / missionaries
c. Puritan / Salem
d. banished / Rhode Island / accepted
e. Maryland
f. Pennsylvania
g. Amish
h. Mormons

Before reading

Page 59 – exercise 1

1. with her shame.
2. her grave would bear the sign of her sin.
3. to leave the Puritan settlement.
4. lived in the Puritan settlement.
5. in a small thatched cottage near the seashore and far from the Puritan settlement.
6. with the needle.
7. contributions to charity to help the poor.

CHAPTER FIVE

Page 65 – exercise 1

1. C   **2.** A   **3.** B   **4.** D   **5.** A   **6.** C
7. B   **8.** D   **9.** A   **10.** C

Page 65 – exercise 2

1. was not allowed
2. were brought
3. in spite of her
4. turned down Hester's
5. was accused of being
6. is not as (so) easy
7. hand was badly

Page 67 – exercise 3A

1. d   **2.** f   **3.** b   **4.** a   **5.** c   **6.** e

Page 67 – exercise 3B

a. came out at
b. come out in the wash
c. coming out of the blue
d. coming out of its ears
e. came out on top
f. came out badly

Page 68 exercises 4-7

Open answers.

The Occult and Witchcraft

Page 71 – exercise 1

1. having to do with secret, mysterious, or supernatural beliefs, events and predictions
2. part of the occult lore
3. occult rituals
4. persecuted and executed witches
5. had magic powers to cast spells, curses, and make bad things happen
6. is still practiced today

CHAPTER SIX

Page 78 – exercise 1

1. D 2. A 3. B 4. C 5. B 6. D

Page 79 – exercise 2

1. had not been
2. would not have married
3. had listened
4. would have remained
5. would have trusted
6. had known
7. had not sent
8. would not have happened
9. had avoided
10. would have been
11. had decided
12. would not have disgraced

Page 80 – exercise 3

1. the (the guests) 2. ✓ 3. ✓ 4. been
5. he 6. ✓ 7. of 8. to (did not to)
9. ✓ 10. to 11. at 12. to (to Hester)
13. ✓ 14. with 15. on

Salem and Witchcraft

Page 85 – exercise 1

1. witchcraft 2. seventeenth
3. adolescent/teenage 4. voodoo
5. from 6. strangely 7. doctor
8. bewitched 9. accused 10. panic
11. devil 12. floor 13. people
14. prison 15. practicing 16. Nineteen
17. wife 18. court 19. over

Before reading

Page 86 – exercise 1

1. C 2. A 3. B 4. C 5. A

CHAPTER SEVEN

Page 94 – exercise 1

a. Chillingworth had chosen the reverend as his spiritual guide, and when the reverend's health began to fail, Chillingworth became his medical adviser. The physician got to know his patient very well, and after some time they shared the same house. Chillingworth was always present in the reverend's life.

b. Because Chillingworth suspected that the reverend was hiding a terrible secret, perhaps the secret that he was desperately trying to discover: the identity of Hester's lover.

c. He underwent a transformation — his face became ugly and evil, and a ghastly light burned in his eyes.

d. Yes, he was aware of an evil presence in his life, but he was not able to recognize his enemy.

e. Dimmesdale exploded in anger after Chillingworth's statement that the reverend's bodily disease was only a symptom of a spiritual ailment, which he should tell his physician about.
Chillingworth remained calm with the reverend, but when Dimmesdale rushed out of the room, Chillingworth was glad that such an explosion of anger had happened.

f. Because of something he had discovered on the reverend's chest while he was sleeping.

Page 95 – exercise 2

a. Well, an addition to the old port has been built recently.

b. The ships are unloaded with new machinery, and not by hand.

c. The downtown area has been greatly expanded.

d. A new town hall is being built near the river.

e. It will probably be finished in the spring.

f. A new hospital was opened at the east end of town by Dr John Peabody, the surgeon.

g. It is directed by his brother, William.

Page 96 – exercise 3

Both men were intelligent and learned.
Chillingworth before his suspicions: learned, intelligent, scholarly, kindly, upright, calm
Chillingworth after his suspicions: ugly, suspicious, enemy in disguise, evil, deceiver, wary

Reverend Dimmesdale all through the story: learned, intelligent, eloquent speaker, passionate, sickly, admired, sensitive, trusted no one, meditative, thin, troubled, pale, religious

The Word "Witch"

Page 98 – exercise 1

1. C **2.** A **3.** D **4.** C **5.** A **6.** B

CHAPTER EIGHT

Page 105 – exercise 1

a. Chillingworth had a greater understanding of Dimmesdale's soul and he manipulated the reverend as he wanted. The minister felt an evil influence in his life but he did not know its real nature. However, externally everything seemed the same, and their habits of social familiarity gave the physician a chance to perfect his revenge on his unsuspecting victim.

b. He was able to understand the sinners of his congregation, since he, too, carried a heavy burden in his heart. The anguish of his daily life kept alive his great power of communicating emotion to his congregation.

c. He told his congregation that he was vile and the worst of sinners, knowing that his vague confession would have the opposite effect on his congregation. In effect, his congregation appreciated him even more!

d. Because he had been driven by the impulses of Remorse and Cowardice: Remorse pushed him to confession, while Cowardice pulled him back.

e. He seemed surprised and pleased to see them. He immediately wanted all three of them to stand together on the platform. Hester was holding Pearl's hand and the minister took Pearl's other hand to form a chain that gave warmth to his half-torpid system. A bright light lit up the sky and the reverend saw an immense letter "A" marked with lines of red light.

f. He asked her if she knew him, and then told her that Chillingworth filled him with horror and that he hated him.

Page 105 – exercise 2

1. D **2.** B **3.** C **4.** A **5.** F **6.** C **7.** D **8.** C **9.** E

Page 105 – exercise 3

1. realized/knew **2.** alone **3.** free/able **4.** isolated/avoided **5.** contact **6.** sinner **7.** taking **8.** away **9.** meeting **10.** convince **11.** God's **12.** adviser **13.** alone **14.** lived **15.** transformation/change **16.** hiding **17.** soul **18.** congregation **19.** whipped **20.** penance **21.** night **22.** saw

Page 106 – exercise 4

Open answer.

Page 107 – exercise 5

a. Where **b.** While **c.** Why **d.** Who **e.** Without **f.** Whom **g.** When/Why

Page 107 – exercises 6-7

Possible answers:
Famous people in literature: Dr Jekyll in Robert Louis Stevenson's *Dr Jekyll and Mr Hyde* and Don Quixote in Miguel de Cervantes' *Don Quixote de la Mancha*.
A famous person in history: Adolf Hitler

Boston, Heart of the American Revolution

Page 110 – exercise 1

a. False – The American Revolution began in Massachusetts in 1775.
b. True
c. False – During the Boston Tea Party, a group of Bostonians disguised as Indians threw 342 crates of tea into Boston Harbor.
d. False – British soldiers killed five colonists during the Boston Massacre.
e. True
f. False – The first shots of the American Revolution were fired in Lexington, in April 1775.
g. True

CHAPTER NINE

Page 117 – exercise 1

1. D **2.** B **3.** D **4.** C **5.** A **6.** B

Page 118 – exercise 2

a. the French **b.** the blind **c.** the supernatural **d.** the elderly **e.** young **f.** the rich/the poor

Page 119 – exercise 3

Open answer.

Page 119 – exercise 4

single parent — because she had a
child and no husband
community volunteer — because she
helps the poor and the sick of her
community

Page 120 – exercise 5

no one's business but her own

Page 120 – exercise 6

a. "'You both have been here before,
but I was not with you. Let us
stand all three together.'" He was
not with them because that was
his own cowardly choice. At this
point, standing together had no
real meaning, only perhaps to
experience a mock punishment.

b. "The minister knew — subtle, but
remorseful hypocrite that he
was — how his vague confession
would be viewed. He spoke the
truth and transformed it into a
falsehood." Dimmesdale knew
that by accusing himself with
symbolic language, this would be
misunderstood and interpreted as
an act of humility, therefore his
"partial confession" served two
purposes: first, he was able to
speak the "truth" and lighten his
conscience; second, he was able
to gain an even better reputation
in the eyes of his congregation.
We must remember that public
opinion was of utmost
importance to the reverend.

c. "'This child has come from the
hand of God to work in many
ways upon the mother's heart. It
was meant to be a blessing; the
one blessing in her life! This
child was meant to keep her
mother's soul alive, and to
preserve her from blacker depths
of sin. Therefore, it is good for
this poor, sinful woman to care
for the child. The child will
remind her of her fall. Let us
follow God's wish.'" In this
scene, Dimmesdale, Hester and
Pearl were together for the first
time since Hester had been on the
scaffold three years ago. This was
a moment of great hardship for
Hester, and Dimmesdale knew
this. It would have been an
occasion for him to assume his
responsibility in the matter. Yet
he continued to conceal his secret
and let all the shame, ignominy
and humiliation fall only on
Hester. Although he did intervene
in her favor, he was careful to
remain out of the story.
Chillingworth, Reverend Wilson
and the governor complimented
him on his intervention!

d. *Possible answers*:
At the beginning of the story, he
and the other town leaders
questioned Hester. The reverend
asked her to confess the name of
her lover and have no pity for
him. When she refused to reveal
the name, the reverend "moved
back with a long sigh", which was
most likely a sigh of relief.

e. ambition, cowardice, remorse and
hypocrisy

Salem Today

Page 122 – exercise 1

a. False – Salem's Indian name was Naumkeag, which meant "City of Peace."
b. True
c. False – Nearly one third of the city is designated as park land and open space.
d. True
e. False – There are seven important "witch museums" in Salem.
f. False – Jonathan Corwin was the judge during the witchcraft trials.

Before reading

Page 123 – exercise 1

1. A 2. C 3. B 4. C 5. A

CHAPTER TEN

Page 130 – exercise 1

a. Because she wanted to meet Reverend Dimmesdale and reveal Chillingworth's real identity to him.
b. She told her that she met him once in her life and the scarlet letter was his mark.
c. Because they had been separated for a very long time.
d. He was shocked, furious and horrified.
e. She advised him to leave Boston and go somewhere else, where he could start a new life.
f. *Open answer.*

Page 130 – exercise 2

a. The minister asked Hester if she had found peace.
b. The reverend said that if he had been a man without a conscience, he might have found peace.
c. Hester said that the people revered him and that he had certainly worked well among them.
d. Hester assured him that he had a friend in her.
e. She assured him that she had always been truthful, but in that circumstance she had had no choice.
f. She begged Arthur to forgive her.
g. She whispered that he would not go alone.

Page 131 – exercise 3

a. None / no **b.** Nowhere
c. None / nothing **d.** Nowhere / none
e. Nothing / nowhere **f.** None / no one

Page 132 – exercise 4

Possible answers:
Hester: The devil tempted her to commit adultery.
Pearl: She was seen as the "child of the devil", a living sin. Even Hester believed that there might be something strange about her child.
Reverend Dimmesdale: Like Hester, he too was tempted by the devil to commit adultery. Being a Puritan minister, he was more closely involved with the forces of good and evil. The presence of Chillingworth could certainly be compared to a diabolic presence in the reverend's life.

Roger Chillingworth: The devil seemed to have possessed Roger Chillingworth. His obsession transformed him into a fiend without any human qualities.

Mrs Hibbins: She practiced witchcraft.

Page 132 – exercise 5

Open answer.

CHAPTER ELEVEN

Page 141 – exercise 1

1. D 2. A 3. B 4. C 5. B 6. D
7. A 8. B 9. C 10. B

Page 142 – exercise 2

1. freed 2. strength 3. enjoyment
4. energetic 5. scornful 6. extremely
7. hopeful 8. startled 9. persecution
10. solution

Page 142 – exercise 3

1. C 2. H 3. A 4. D 5. F 6. B 7. E
Sentence G is not used.

Page 143 – exercise 4A

1. d 2. e 3. a 4. b 5. c 6. f

Page 143 – exercise 4B

a. looked down on
b. look it over
c. look alike
d. look after
e. look it up
f. looked forward to

Page 144 – exercise 5

Hester
Psychological Changes: felt free, happy, hopeful, her heart was light.

Physical Changes: a smile appeared on her face; her sex, youth and beauty all came back.

Reverend Dimmesdale
Psychological Changes: began to feel a strange enjoyment, a sense of exhilaration and relief; felt strangely mischievous; was tempted to do something wild or wicked; strange desire to be scornful and bitter, to ridicule all that was good and holy; felt spiteful and unkind.
Physical Changes: felt a surge of physical energy; felt strong and energetic; ate with a good appetite; showed energy during the procession.

Page 144 – exercise 6

Open answers.

Page 145 – exercise 7

Possible answers:
stomach-ache / asthma / skin rash / colitis / fainting / dizziness

Page 145 – exercise 8

Open answers.

CHAPTER TWELVE

Page 152 – exercise 1

a. He paused, turned towards the scaffold, stretched out his arms and called Hester and Pearl to him.
b. He caught the minister's arm and tried to stop him.
c. He finally confessed. He told them that at last he was on the scaffold where he should have been seven years ago with Hester. He called himself a sinner.

d. He tore away his ministerial band and most of the spectators saw that he too had a scarlet letter imprinted in his flesh.
Others denied having seen anything on his breast. They also said that his dying words did not acknowledge a connection with Hester's scarlet letter.

e. They disappeared and no one knew where they had gone.

f. She had gone to another land where she lived in great comfort and wealth.

g. She returned because Boston was the place of her sin, her sorrow and her penance. She devoted her life to comforting and counselling wretched women.

Page 152 – exercise 2

1. Election **2.** weak **3.** barely
4. stood **5.** stretched **6.** arms
7. calling **8.** tried **9.** determined
10. confess **11.** townspeople
12. father **13.** child **14.** passionate
15. tore **16.** band **17.** breast
18. scarlet letter **19.** flesh
20. horror-stricken **21.** death
22. withered **23.** away **24.** absence
25. Boston **26.** free **27.** life
28. helping **29.** comforting
30. women **31.** life **32.** gifts
33. buried **34.** Chapel **35.** grave
36. inscription **37.** tombstone
38. sable **39.** gules

Page 154 – exercise 3A

a. He did not admit speaking to the witch.

b. I suggested giving her monetary help.

c. Hester remembered going to the forest alone.

Page 154 – exercise 3B

a. dread going
b. adore listening
c. avoid walking
d. risk being/arriving
e. start studying

Page 154 – exercise 4

Open answer.

Page 155 – exercise 5

Because he knew that he was a dying man and he wanted to take the shame upon himself, since this was the right thing to do.

Page 155 – exercise 6

There are several possible interpretations for this:

a. He wanted to remove himself from his shame by referring to another person, although he was talking about himself.

b. He wanted to continue being a subtle hypocrite, by speaking in the third person, thereby not involving himself directly.

c. He was in a very confused mental state, and he had temporarily "stepped out" of his body. In other words, the pious reverend was talking about the sinner — the two sides of the reverend's personality.

Page 155 – exercises 7-8

Open answers.

Page 155 – exercise 9

Suggested answer:
Because Chillingworth is not seen by Hawthorne as a human being, but as an ugly weed or fiend. The expression "withered up" is very appropriate because he devoted part of his life to studying plants, herbs and weeds.

Page 156 – exercise 10

Possible answers:
St Joan of Arc, Florence Nightingale, Harriet Tubman, Emmeline Pankhurst, Mother Teresa of Calcutta.

Page 156 – exercises 11-12

Open answers.

Page 156 – exercise 13

Things that changed:
a. The film does not begin with the Puritan prison and Hester on the scaffold. It begins with Hester's first meeting with Reverend Dimmesdale and their consequent intimacy.
b. Several episodes have been eliminated.
c. The ending shows Hester being rescued from the scaffold by an energetic reverend, who takes her and Pearl away from Boston to live elsewhere. They live together happily for a few years until Dimmesdale's death.

Things that were the same:
a. The setting in Puritan Boston was the same.
b. Chillingworth's persecution, although not as intense, was similar.

Page 156 – exercise 14

Possible answers:
assertive, admirable, active, adaptable, able, adept, artful, alienated, altruistic, attractive, aware, articulate, audacious, American

The Importance of *The Scarlet Letter* in American Literature

Page 160 – exercise 1

1. a woman is the heroine
2. what America would one day become
3. wild and majestic
4. the good opinion of society
5. he used symbolic language which was misunderstood
6. transformed him into a devil

1

1. C   2. D   3. A   4. B   5. D
6. B   7. A   8. C   9. D   10. B
11. C   12. D

2

1. G   2. B   3. F   4. E   5. H
6. C   7. D   8. A   9. F   10. E
11. F   12. C   13. D   14. C

3

1. g   2. h   3. a   4. j   5. b
6. i   7. d   8. e   9. c   10. f

4

a. Nathaniel Hawthorne.
b. He was born in Salem, Massachusetts in 1804.
c. While still at college, he decided to become a writer. After graduating, he studied the Puritans and their history. His first novel *Fanshawe* was not a success. *The Scarlet Letter* was his masterpiece and was published in 1850. He also wrote *The House of the Seven Gables* and *The Blithedale Romance*. In 1853 he was appointed US consul in Liverpool and Manchester, England.
d. The Puritans were a Protestant reform movement. They wanted to purify the Church of all Roman Catholic influence. They believed in predestination. They observed austere morality and, dress and behavior.
e. Devotion to work and business enterprise. It is at the root of modern American society.
f. They were trials against "bewitched" people in Salem in 1692. It caused general hysteria among the townspeople and 19 people were hanged and over 100 put in prison.

5

a. F – The child was about 3 months old.
b. T
c. F – She refused to reveal it.
d. F – He wanted to discover who her lover was.
e. F – She was ostracized.
f. F – Governor Bellingham wanted to take Pearl away from Hester.
g. T
h. F – He became obsessed with Reverend Dimmesdale.
i. T
j. T
k. F – Reverend Dimmesdale died on the scaffold during the election sermon.

6

a. Reverend Dimmesdale
b. Hester
c. Chillingworth
d. Pearl
e. Female spectator
f. The beadle
g. Chillingworth
h. Dimmesdale
i. Hester
j. Hester

NOTES

Black Cat English Readers

Level 1
Peter Pan
Zorro!
American Folk Tales
The True Story of Pocahontas
Davy Crockett
Great Expectations NEW!
Rip Van Winkle and The Legend
  of Sleepy Hollow NEW!
The Happy Prince and The Selfish
  Giant NEW!
The American West NEW!
Halloween Horror NEW!

Level 2
Oliver Twist
King Arthur and his Knights
Oscar Wilde's Short Stories
Robin Hood
British and American
  Festivities

Level 3
Alice's Adventures in Wonderland
The Jumping Frog
Hamlet
The Secret Garden
Great English Monarchs and their
  Times

Level 4
The £1,000,000 Bank Note
Jane Eyre
Sherlock Holmes Investigates
Gulliver's Travels
The Strange Case of Dr Jekyll
  and Mr Hyde
Classic Detective Stories
The Phantom of the Opera
Alien at School
Romeo and Juliet
Treasure Island

Level 5
A Christmas Carol
The Tragedy of Dr Faustus
Washington Square
A Midsummer Night's Dream
American Horror
Much Ado About Nothing
The Canterbury Tales
Dracula
The Last of the Mohicans
The Big Mistake and Other Stories

Level 6
Frankenstein
Pride and Prejudice
Robinson Crusoe
A Tale of Two Cities
The X-Files : Squeeze
Emma NEW!
The Scarlet Letter NEW!
Tess of the d'Urbervilles NEW!
The Murders in the Rue Morgue
  and The Purloined Letter NEW!
The Problem of Cell 13 NEW!

BLACK CAT ENGLISH CLUB
Membership Application Form

BLACK CAT ENGLISH CLUB is for those who love English reading and seek for better English to share and learn with fun together.

Benefits offered: - *Membership Card*   - *English learning activities*
                         - *Book discount coupon*   - *Black Cat English Reward Scheme*
                         - *English learning e-forum* - *Surprise gift and more...*

Simply fill out the application form below and fax it back to 2565 1113 or send it back to the address at the back.

Join Now! It's FREE exclusively for readers who have purchased *Black Cat English Readers* !

(Please fill out the form with **BLOCK LETTERS**.)

The title of Black Cat English Reader/book set that you have purchased: _____

English Name: _____ (Surname) _____ (Given Name)

Chinese Name: _____

Address:

Tel: _____   Fax: _____

Email: _____
(Login password for e-forum will be sent to this email address.)

Sex: ❏ Male   ❏ Female

Education Background: ❏ Primary 1-3   ❏ Primary 4-6   ❏ Junior Secondary Education (F1-3)
                     ❏ Senior Secondary Education (F4-5)   ❏ Matriculation
                     ❏ College   ❏ University or above

Age: ❏ 6 - 9   ❏ 10 - 12   ❏ 13 - 15   ❏ 16 - 18   ❏ 19 - 24   ❏ 25 - 34
     ❏ 35 - 44   ❏ 45 - 54   ❏ 55 or above

Occupation: ❏ Student   ❏ Teacher   ❏ White Collar   ❏ Blue Collar
             ❏ Professional   ❏ Manager   ❏ Business Owner   ❏ Housewife
             ❏ Others (please specify: _____)

As a member, what would you like **BLACK CAT ENGLISH CLUB** to offer:

❏ Member gathering/ party   ❏ English class with native teacher   ❏ English competition
❏ Newsletter   ❏ Online sharing   ❏ Book fair
❏ Book discount   ❏ Others (please specify: _____)

Other suggestions to **BLACK CAT ENGLISH CLUB**: _____

Please sign here: _____   (Date: _____)

Visit us at Quality English Learning Online http://publish.commercialpress.com.hk/qel

BLACK CAT ENGLISH CLUB
The Commercial Press (Hong Kong) Ltd.
9/F, Eastern Central Plaza,
3 Yiu Hing Road, Shau Kei Wan,
Hong Kong